The Treatment of Head Injuries
in the Thirty Years' War (1618-1648)

JOANNIS SCULTETUS AND HIS AGE

The Treatment of Head Injuries in the Thirty Years' War (1618-1648)

JOANNIS SCULTETUS AND HIS AGE

LOUIS BAKAY, M.D., F.A.C.S.

Professor of Surgery (Neurosurgery) and Head
Division of Neurosurgery
State University of New York at Buffalo, School of Medicine
Buffalo, New York

INDIANAPOLIS MARION CO. PUBLIC LIBRARY

CHARLES C THOMAS · PUBLISHER
Springfield · Illinois · U.S.A.

Published and Distributed Throughout the World by

CHARLES C THOMAS • PUBLISHER

BANNERSTONE HOUSE

301-327 East Lawrence Avenue, Springfield, Illinois, U.S.A.

NATCHEZ PLANTATION HOUSE

735 North Atlantic Boulevard, Fort Lauderdale, Florida, U.S.A.

With THOMAS BOOKS *careful attention is given to all details of manufacturing and design. It is the Publisher's desire to present books that are satisfactory as to their physical qualities and artistic possibilities and appropriate for their particular use.* THOMAS BOOKS *will be true to those laws of quality that assure a good name and good will.*

Printed in the United States of America

C-1

Dedicated to the memory of all the Bakay's de Bakabánya et Kozárvár, nobles of Hungary and Transylvania, soldiers, pastors, surgeons, patriots. . . .

PREFACE

*I*T was the dawn of the modern age, as we know it, with its nationalism, religious freedom, individual commerce and trade patterns, and military organization. It also heralded the emergence of the common man from the dark recesses of history preserved until then for the deeds of princes, conquerors, saints, and villains. The Thirty Years' War, or rather the unbearable internal pressure that led to its violent and prolonged eruption in the first half of the seventeenth century, changed every aspect of life in the Western World. Its effect is still noticeable. Whether this era, the Modern Age, is now coming to an end to be replaced by a new period of history is not yet clear, but our intellectual world is still heavily rooted in the sixteenth through the seventeenth century.

It was then that modern science emerged: Francis Bacon with his methodology of empirism, the mathematical reasoning of Descartes, Galileo's concept of the solar system, and Kepler's laws of planetary motion, to name only a few spectacular accomplishments. These men knew that they were opening a new chapter in the history of mankind; they perceived the role of science in the future, and many even worried about the changes and dangers it would introduce into the life of man, as did Francis Bacon.

Medicine was no exception. Vesalius described man's body accurately for the first time. Harvey discovered the circulation of blood and Paré laid down the foundation of modern surgery. Less is known of the beginnings of modern neurosurgery or, to be more precise, that of the treatment of craniocerebral trauma. I thought it would be interesting to approach neurosurgery through the eyes and minds of men of the seventeenth century. I also thought it necessary to give a brief sketch of the war and its participants. No man can be disassociated from the time in which he lives and works, particularly when the times are as turbulent and agonizing as those of the Thirty Years' War—or ours for that matter.

Among the original sources to this book, the text of the *Armamentarium Chirurgicum* of Joannis Scultetus was translated from the 1666 Frankfurt edition. This is a reedition of the first edition of 1653 with the original Latin text. The translation is my own and, therefore, I am responsible for any error that might have occurred. I would like to express my gratitude to the good Piarist fathers of Budapest who showed great patience and perseverance many years ago to teach Latin and Greek to one of their more recalcitrant students. I tried to keep verbatim to the original, particularly in the passages between quotation marks. This was not always possible; occasional, slight changes in translation were necessary because of the sometimes ponderous baroque phraseology of the author and frequent repetitions.

The work of Berengario da Carpi was studied in the third edition of his *Tractatus Perutilis et Completus de Fractura Cranei* (Venice, 1535), then in the Boston Medical Library. Old notes taken on Fabricius Hildanus and a late seventeenth century edition of his *Observationum et Curationum Chirurgicum Centuria* take me back to days spent at the Library of the Medical Faculty of the Royal Hungarian "Petrus Pázmány" University of Budapest.

Most of the neurosurgical lore of Ambroise Paré was extracted from Wallace Hamby's faithful rendition of *The Case Reports and Autopsy Records of Ambroise Paré*, published in 1960 by Charles C Thomas, Publisher, and his translations of the monumental *Oeuvres Complètes d'Ambroise Paré Révues et Collectionnées sur Toutes les Éditions avec les Variantes par J. F. Malgaigne* (Paris, 1840-41).

There are many German editions, old and new, of Grimmelshausen's *Der Abenteuerliche Simplicissimus*. Several were used. Again, the translation is mine. His language is so vivid and clear that a word-by-word translation was possible and quite acceptable for modern reading.

I am indebted to Mr. Joseph A. Dommer for most of the photographic work of the illustrations, a difficult and painstaking undertaking which involved the reproduction of old, sometimes faded and foxed prints and pages.

LOUIS BAKAY

Buffalo, New York

CONTENTS

The Treatment of Head Injuries
in the Thirty Years' War (1618-1648)

JOANNIS SCULTETUS AND HIS AGE

Chapter 1

THE SOURCES

◇◇

*O*FTEN, when dealing with events in past history, whether social, political, or scientific, we are inclined to judge such events with the hindsight that today's knowledge affords. Such hindsight can, of course, allow us an analysis of past events that can be indispensable. Where we often fail is not taking into consideration the entire milieu of an age—the social and political atmosphere of an era as a backdrop behind one particular aspect of life.

In this particular instance I propose to subject neurosurgery in the first half of the seventeenth century (that for practical purposes amounted to the treatment of head injuries) to just such a broad scrutiny. I used as my guides to this era three remarkable men: Joannis Scultetus, Hans von Grimmelshausen, and Jacques Callot.

The heart of the matter, our source of surgical treatment, is Joannis Scultetus, a remarkable physician and scientific writer, one of the great surgeons of all ages. The turbulent time in which he worked is described by Grimmelshausen with great literary skill in the novel *Simplicissimus,* a masterpiece in the modern sense, full of psychological symbolisms but meticulously accurate as an eyewitness account of the Thirty Years' War. And finally, in his series *Les Misères et les Mal-Heurs de la Guerre,* the artist who expressed pictorially the anguish and cruelty of life in those days is France's greatest etcher, Jacques Callot.

Who were these men?

Johann Schultes, commonly called Joannis Scultetus, was born in the city of Ulm, in Swabia, on the shores of the Danube on October 12, 1595. He left for Italy at the early age of fifteen and studied medicine in Padua under the famous Fabricius ab Aquapendente and Adriaan van den Spieghel, a Belgian surgeon and anatomist of prominence. Scultetus served as prosector during his studies. Eventually he received his doctorate in medicine, surgery, and philosophy in 1621. During the next few years he practiced medicine briefly in Padua, then in Vienna, and, as a military surgeon, in the Imperial Army in Germany during the Thirty Years' War. Finally, in his thirties he settled down in his hometown and became city physician of Ulm. He remained there for the rest of his life. He died in 1645 in Stuttgart where he was called to see a patient in consultation.[1, 2]

A bold and imaginative surgeon, Scultetus was widely known in his relatively brief life in Germany and the adjacent countries. Some of the surgical principles he developed are still practiced, and the Scultetus binder preserved his name to our own age. His only known major work, the *Armamentarium Chirurgicum,* appeared eight years after his death. It was published by his nephew, Joannis Scultetus, the Younger, in 1653, and printed in Ulm by Balthasar Kühnen. It became immediately and immensely popular. It was reprinted and translated many times. Already in 1656 it was republished in The Hague (*Armamentarium Chirurgicum,* The Hague, Adrian Vlacq); a French edition followed (*L'Arcenal de Chirurgie de Jean Scultet,* Lyon, d'Antoine Galien, 1674). This was "mis en Francois par Messire Francois Deboze," the text being "renovvellé, corrigé, et avgmenté." It also contained as an additional thrill "la description d'un Monstre humain exposé à Lyon le 5 de Mars 1671." It was "faithfully Englished" in 1674 (*The Chyrurgeons Store-House,* by E. B., London, John Starkey). Innumerable editions followed well to the end of the eighteenth century.

In every new translation and edition of the *Armamentarium Chirurgicum,* new chapters were added to the original text, as well as new illustrations to keep it up to date and to conform with the personal views of the various editors. Sometimes this fact was referred to in the title page (*Armamentarium Chirurgicum Ioannis Sculteti, Renovatum et Auctum*), but frequently it was not. To name an example, description and plates dealing with plastic surgery of the face after the method of Tagliacozzi (1545-1599) appear in the edition printed in Holland in 1741. Although Tagliacozzi did some pioneering work on the surgery of deformities by transplantation (*De Curtorum Chirurgia per*

Insitionem), the first treatise devoted exclusively to the theory
and practice of the art appeared in Venice in 1597.[3] Although
this had occurred several decades before the first edition of
the *Armamentarium,* Scultetus was completely unaware of it. I
therefore considered it important to translate an early version
in order to obtain the unadulterated views and methods of
Scultetus and the flavor of surgery as it was practiced during the
Thirty Years' War.

The first edition of Scultetus's work is in folio (most subsequent editions and translations are in small octavo), with forty-
three splendidly engraved plates. Its title page contains the following floridly baroque text: "Cheiroplotheke (graece), Seu Armamentarium Chirurgicum XLIII Tabvlis aeri elegantissime
incisis, nec antehac visis, exornatum. Opus posthumum, Medici-
nae pariter as Chirurgiae Studiosis perutile & necessarium, in
quo tot. tam veterum ac recetiorvm instrumenta ab authore cor-
recta, quam noviter ab ipso inventa, quot fere hodie ad usitatas
operationes manuales feliciter peragendas requiruntur. Nunc
primum in lucem editum. Studio et Opera Joannis Sculteti, Au-
thoris ex fratre Nepotis. Cum triplici Instrumentorum, Curationum, rerumque memorabilium Indice."

This, then, combines a title with all necessary information,
similar to the description which appears on the jacket of a modern medical book. It tells that the book is illustrated with "ele-
gant engravings." Although it is a posthumous work, edited by
the author's nephew, it contains original information on instruments, some improved, others newly invented, to be used fruit-
fully in manual operations.

The title of later, but otherwise unchanged editions, was simpler and better composed (Fig. 1). The printing was good, the
text entirely in Latin with only the names of patients, place
names, and a very rare, occasional phrase in German gothic type
(Fig. 2). There is little in way of ornamentation, except for
rather trivial headpieces of garlands of geometrical designs over
the principal chapter headings, ornamental first letters, and an
occasional symbolic tailpiece. These latter sometimes illustrate
the crowned head of a lion with a somewhat human face.
Nesmith[4] explains its meaning. To primitive peoples, the mane

ARMAMENTARIVM
CHIRVRGICVM
BIPARTITVM,

Studioq; & opera

D. JOANNIS SCVLTETI VLMENSIS,

Reipubl. Patriæ Physici ordinarij, reformatum,
correctum & auctum.

Cum LVI. Tabulis, sive Figuris æneis

novis accuratissimis.

Vt &

Tribus Indicibus absolutissimis,

INSTRUMENTORUM SCILICET, OBSERVATIONUM,
ET RERUM NOTABILIUM.

FRANCOFVRTI,
Sumptibus Viduæ Joan. **Gerlini, Bibliop.** Ulm.
Typis JOANNIS GERLINI

ANNO M DC LXVI.

Figure 1. Title page of the 1666 Frankfurt edition of Scultetus' *Armamentarium Chirurgicum.*

Concuffio cerebri & tumor brachii fuppuratus.

ANNO M.DC.XXVII. Menfe Novembris, *Johannes* Seinlen / Oppingenfis ex agro Ulmenfi,ruftici cujusdam Nellingæ famulus,temperamenti calidi & humidi in ædibus Marci Feyhels fuit , in quibus more loci juvenculæ & ancillæ filum duxerunt, penfumque fuum abfolverunt. Hic verò nofter *Johannes* cum aliqua juvencularum tum temporis in hypocaufto lufit. Huic reliquæ præfentes juvenculæ feriò imperarunt,ut tales nugas relinqueret, fonft werde ihm der Baum geftellt werden / cujus pœnæ Proceffus talis eft : Detinent aliquem corpore inverfo , ut capite refpiciat terram, pedibus verò fufpenfum fubitò in terram iterum remittunt, ut caput concutiatur. Hoc perpetrarunt etiam juvenculæ in noftro ægroto , quia non obtemperavit, ufque dum fanguis è naribus & auribus profluxerit , atque humi proftratus inftar mortui jacuerit. Videntes prædictæ juvenculæ dubium hunc actum, humi proftratum aqua frigida ftatim afperferunt , quo revocentur illius fpiritus. Hic aquâ perfufus , quafi à morte revocatus , furrexit , de magnoque finiftri brachii & totius capitis dolore conqueftus difceffit. Secundo die , præfente hoc capitis ac brachii dolore , æger nihilominus frumentum ventilavit. Tertio & quarto pejus habuit , ita ut propter febrem & motus totius convulfivos lecto decumbere coactus fuerit. Sexto morbi die curru petiit Oppingam. Septimo mater accerfivit Chirurgos. Die x. xi. xii. xiii. & xiv. die æger antedictis convulfionibus vexabatur. Die xv. mater decumbentis filii urinam transmifit Clariffimo Domino Doctori , *N. Klebfattelio* , *Medico Geislingenfium indefeffo*, qui præfcripfit pulverem contra cafum (ad diffolvendum fanguinem grumofum) in mixtura fyrupi acetofitatis citri & acetofæ cum aqua pimpinellæ fumendum. Hinc æger mutus & furdus ufque ad vigefimum quartum diem laboravit comate : de qua aphonia ita vaticinatus eft Hippocrates Sect. 7. aphor. 58.

Figure 2. A typical page from the *Armamentarium Chirurgicum.*

of the lion resembled rays of the sun, and the design became a symbol for Light. The book which it adorns must therefore be the vehicle of Truth, or at least a "brave attempt to lift the Darkness of (medical) Ignorance."

The engraved illustrations are explicit and technically excellent. They were redrawn by Jonas Arnold after drawings made by Scultetus and engraved by Jeremias Renner. Almost every plate carries the sign "Jonas Arnold delineavit." One must only compare these plates with the crude woodcuts of the book of Berengario da Carpi on head injuries to realize the advance in book illustrations during the intervening century.

The book is dedicated to the "Most Magnificent, Noble, Generous, Learned and Prudent Council of Twelves and to the Consuls and Senators of the Imperial Republic of Ulm" ("Magnificis, Nobilissimis, Amplissimis, Consultissimis & Prudentissimis Dnn. Duum-Viris, Consulibus, AC Senatoribus Inclytae Reipubl. Imperialis Ulmensis"). In other words, to the city fathers. A preface by the nephew, Johannes Scultetus the Younger, follows; it is a touching tribute to his uncle, "of pious memory, first led by the admirable direction of God, devoted his mind to the study of sickness from his youth without vanity. . . . He attained no small glory in the fortuitous performance of surgical operations." "The ancients discovered much but left much more to be discovered." "He (Scultetus) chose that miracle of Nature, Man's body, to be his subject and studied it with great delight; he collected every day new observations and wrote them down with the intent of publishing them one day . . . God disposed otherwise and upon his untimely departure from life . . . I, having been observant to him and of the same profession . . . felt obliged to perform the desire of the deceased." He then dedicates the book to the city officials of Ulm who were instrumental in sending him for a study course of three years in the Venetian Republic and admitted him to the Council of Physicians upon his return. It is clear that the nephew followed his uncle's footsteps. He also trained to be a physician at the University of Padua and later became a city physician in Ulm, as well as the literary executor of the older Scultetus.

The first portion of the book deals with surgical instruments. The second part forms an amply illustrated description of surgical operations, their technique, and indication. These first two parts are entitled "Surgery." It is lucidly organized and follows the anatomy of the body from head to legs with special chapters devoted to the application of bandages and the setting of fractures. This "Surgery" comprises 152 pages in the 1666 Frankfurt edition. Thirty of the 152 pages deal with head injuries, their treatment, and the description of primarily neurosurgical instruments.

The second part of the book is entitled "Observations"; it includes one hundred detailed case histories. Again, 31 of the 140 pages, or twenty-three out of the one hundred histories, are devoted to injuries of the skull and brain. One might then come to the somewhat surprising conclusion that neurosurgery, or more precisely, treatment of head trauma, in the first half of the seventeenth century represented a very significant portion of all surgical procedures.

The life, civilian and military, with all its horrors, is graphically described by Grimmelshausen in his book *Simplicissimus.* This, the greatest German novel of the seventeenth century, is partly autobiographical. Hans Jakob Christoffel von Grimmelshausen was born in Hesse sometime between 1610 and 1620. It is fairly well established that he lost his parents and family in the sack of Gelnhausen by Hessian troops. He was then carried away as a child as what would be called these days a mascot by marauding, probably by Croatian troops. At the age of seventeen he joined the Imperial Army as a dragoon or musketeer. The difference between the two must have been slight because he mentions that "when a dragoon is unhorsed, he leaps to his feet as a musketeer." He lived the harsh life of a common soldier through many engagements, participated in the seige of Magdeburg in 1636, the battle of Wittstock, and the campaigns in Westfalen and the Upper Rhine. Eventually, he obtained the position of regimental secretary, but remained in military service until the end of the war in 1648. He then married and became steward on a large estate. Later he became magistrate and tax collector, and died in the small town of Renchen, in the Bishopric of Strasbourg on the 17th of August of 1676, again in the midst of war, this time the French-Netherlandish conflict. In the church register of Renchen his death is recorded with the following remark: "Honestus et magno ingenio et eruditione . . . praetor huius loci." ("Honest, ingenious and erudite . . . a magistrate of this community.")

Grimmelshausen began to write after his separation from the army. His greatest work, commonly referred to as *Simplicissimus,* was first published in Mompelgart, by Johann Fillion in 1669. It has the formidable full title of *Der Abenteuerliche Simplicissimus Teutsch—Das ist die Beschreibung des Lebens eines seltsamen Vaganten, genannt Melchior Sternfels von Fuchshaim, wo und welchergestalt er nämlich in diese Welt kommen, was er darin gesehen, gelernet, erfahren und ausgestanden, auch warum er solche wieder freiwillig quittiert. (The adventurous*

German Simplicissimus—The description of the life of a peculiar vagabond, Melchior Sternfels von Fuchshaim by name, where and in what form he was born, what he has seen, learned, experienced and endured in this world and why he voluntarily quit the same.) It is the story of a wild boy experiencing the cruelties, but also the grim humor of the Thirty Years' War. In its later chapters, it is filled with supernatural visions, religious allegories, and remarkably modern psychological symbolism that is still subject to controversial explanations. What we are interested in is Grimmelshausen's firsthand account of life and war. He tells his story well, with keen realism and coarse humor; it is a bitter indictment of war.

The popular illustrations of *Simplicissimus* were first issued in a 1683 edition. They are craftsman-like, but not particularly artistic scenes depicting various aspects of life with fidelity. As a charming example of baroque art and early book illustration, they carry a four-line or six-line stanza at the bottom of the picture describing the happenings. They all start with the word "Schau" ("See"), which was the routine beginning of a verse on leaves of woodcuts depicting stories or historical events and which sold for pennies at fairs. It also started the large pages of illustrated texts turned at the markets by professional story-tellers to their audience as they narrated their stories.

Jacques Callot was born in 1592 in Lorraine where his father was a court official. The young Callot was properly educated, but longed for adventure. As an apprentice in glass painting, he made several attempts to travel to Italy on his own, only to be apprehended and carted back to his family. On one of his escapades, he traveled for months with a gypsy caravan. Eventually his family relented, and he journeyed to Rome where he studied drawing and engraving. After a few years in Rome, he moved on to Florence, the site of his activities for the next ten years. He became one of the greatest draftsmen of all ages and the founder of modern copper engraving. Callot was no mere craftsman in his art but a man of great sensitivity, perception, and universal knowledge. Not only did he dabble in geometry and trigonometry, but he actually studied mathematics with no lesser man than Galileo.[5]

Eventually, in 1621 he returned to Lorraine, settled in Nancy, married, and became an artist of renown at the court of Lorraine. Ill health plagued him, and so did the miseries of war he saw on his travels. He did not have to go far to see it at close range. The war sought him out; Nancy fell, and all Lorraine was devastated by Richelieu's soldiers. The artist decided to flee with his family to Florence, but it was too late. He died, probably of tuberculosis, in Nancy on March 24, 1635, at the age of forty-three.

But, what artistic legacy he left![5, 6]

He etched about fifteen hundred plates in addition to his many sketches, some preserved, many more lost. These etchings were superb, rendering a drama, lightness of movement, and depth of field unknown until then to the previously limited scope of an engraved copperplate. To be sure, many of them represented courtly scenes, allegories, and religious subjects. Some of them depicted military campaigns and sieges in the traditional manner. A series of his etchings, entitled "Exercices militaires," depicted military drills so accurately that they were used for another century or two for courses in tactics in military schools. But most of his etchings dealt with the outcasts of society, gypsies, beggars, artists of the commedia dell'arte of seventeenth century Italy, and the flotsam of war-torn Europe. As Daniel[5] put it, "with Callot a new element appeared, a missing piece known as the common man."

One of his most powerful series of etchings, the "Miseries of War," was prompted by the devastation of his native land, Lorraine, at the hand of Cardinal Richelieu's men, a side show of the Thirty Years' War. It was entitled: "Les Misères et les Mal-Hevrs De la Gverre. Representez Par Iacques Callot, Noble Lorrain. Et mis en lumière Par Israel, son amy. A Paris, 1633. Avec Privilège du Roy." The scenes unfolded by these plates have not been matched by any other artist but Goya. They are a perfect counterpart to the narrative of Grimmelshausen.

Chapter 2

THE WAR

✧✧

*T*HE horrors of the Thirty Years' War! It became a common phrase to express man's inhumanity to man. It was the worst of times, the first half of the seventeenth century. Spain rotted, and the Continent writhed in religious mania and social upheaval. A new era, the Modern Age, was dawning amidst all the turmoil that characterizes the breakdown of old values and the painful birth of a new order. Meanwhile social order, including "divinely ordained" privileges, collapsed. On the top it was a "silken robe smeared with blood," as Voltaire described it in the next century. But at the base of the pyramid, it was the common people who suffered. It was the time when "various groups of beplumed thugs struggled with one another for the exclusive right to their particular Christian version of rape, rapine and ruin."[5]

The Thirty Years' War, starting in 1618 and ending in 1648 with the Peace of Westphalia, is by itself a somewhat misleading historical concept. It was not one uninterrupted war, but rather a complex struggle of dozens of loosely connected conflicts for the European balance of power, mostly between the Habsburgs and various German principalities, but involving also France, Sweden, and other countries.

There is a considerable difference of opinion among historians concerning the whole concept of this war and its impact on Europe. According to the romantic German historiographers of the nineteenth century, the Thirty Years' War was the source of all evil that befell the German nation politically and economically for centuries to come. Others, particularly the British, considered it merely as loosely connected episodes of political turbulence that afflicted the heart of Europe, without definite beginning and end and described only by hindsight as the Thirty Years' War. They also thought that the devastation of land

and loss of population as estimated by later historians was greatly exaggerated. This might be true, but there is no doubt that
the population of Germany was reduced by at least one third
during the war. Starvation was widespread because of lack of
agricultural labor. The fields remained unplowed, and starvation followed. While large cities fared somewhat better, many
villages were destroyed, and some disappeared from the map.
Ravaged by armies that descended like hordes of locusts on the
countryside, morals returned to the level of the darkest of the
Dark Ages; violence and murder were the order of the day (Fig.
3).

While some of the aspects of this series of wars, such as the
occurrence or frequency of famine leading to cannibalism,
might have been overemphasized, there was enough well docu-
mented bestiality. A relatively unbiased eyewitness, Grimmelshausen, described in dramatic details "all Germany in the flames
of war, hunger and pestilence." Bands of marauding soldiers
fell on defenseless villages, killed, tortured, and raped (Fig. 4).
Their senseless cruelty took many forms. Peasants were beaten,
flayed alive, forced to drink the notorious "Swedish drink"—a
vile concoction of unspeakable ingredients, baked alive in
ovens, and killed in many other ways of fiendish imagination.
The people, of course, retaliated. "In those days," wrote Grim-

Figure 3. Fate of the losers. "La Pendaison," a famous etching from the
"Miseries of War," by Jacques Callot (1633).

Figure 4. Murder, pillage, and rape. Detail from an etching by Jacques Callot. (Courtesy Prints Division, The New York Public Library, Astor, Lenox and Tilden Foundations and *Horizon Magazine*.)

melshausen, "rarely did a peasant go into the forest without a firearm," not knowing whether he would be able to return to his village or not. "Many found refuge in the bush and in the mountains, having escaped death on the plains." Guerilla war, perhaps the first guerilla war on a large scale in history, raged. Stragglers or outnumbered groups of soldiers were set upon and mercilessly slain by the insurgents. There is a scene in *Simplicissimus* describing in great detail how a horseman captured by the guerillas was buried alive after his ears and nose were cut off.

It is certainly not true that the Thirty Years' War was called by this name only much later on. Proof to the contrary can be found in the preface of Scultetus's book, published a mere five years after the Peace of Westphalia: "Bellum tricenarium Germanicum, de cujus plagis etiamnunc pène tota gemit Germania & quod Christianus contra Christianum novit, Defensore Deo, vobisque Directoribus, moenia nostra non conquassavit, areas & templa non violavit, pudorem virgineum non constupravit, sed haec omnia constantissima Vestra Tutela defendit, Suma Prudentia conservavit & ingenita sedulitas protexit." ("The Thirty Years' German War of whose wounds almost all of Germany sighed until now, that turned Christian against Christian, but defended by God and you, Leaders (of our city), has not shat-

tered the walls of our city, has not violated its altars and churches, has not ravished the virtue of its virgins; it was defended by
your most steady protection, preserved by your prudence and
protected by your innate zeal.") A somewhat florid piece of ded-
ication, it certainly proves that this war *was* called Thirty Years'
War soon after the armistice. It also points out the fact that the
city of Ulm had not been sacked by the belligerents; however,
life in the immediate vicinity of the town was not free of
strife, as we will see from Scultetus's case histories.

The complexity and political ramifications of this war were
so enormous that it is hardly possible to give an accurate outline
in a brief text. It began with isolated incidents at a time when
no European power wanted war, but the atmosphere was com-
bustible, and a spark set the heart of Europe ablaze. It was the
prototype of modern world conflicts. Trevor-Roper[8] used the
Thirty Years' War as an example in his fascinating essay, "Why
Do Great Wars Begin?"

There was surely enough political tension. By the early seventeenth century, the Counter-Reformation checked the rapid
spread of Protestantism of the previous century. The ideologi-
cal and, indeed, political struggle between Catholicism and Protestantism sharpened, and some of the Protestant powers were re-
conquered. The law of "Cuius regio eius religio" prevailed,
meaning that a whole region, be that a city or country, had to
follow the religion of its ruler. Accordingly, the only tolerated
religion of a given state was subject to change with the personal
belief of a new ruler, who then might have become partner in
a new political alliance with princes of the same faith.

The bulwark of Protestantism was Germany. But this Germany was divided into hundreds of kingdoms, electorates,
duchies, and independent cities. Other Protestant powers included the Netherlands, in a death grip with Spain for its very survival, Sweden, Denmark, and Transylvania. Bohemia and Hungary, while still predominantly Protestant, were subjugated by
the Habsburgs at a rapid rate. England remained aloof.

The protector of Catholicism, and a powerful protector it
was, was the Habsburg empire, both its Spanish and Austrian
branches. They dominated the Pope. They occupied a large part

of Europe: Spain, much of Italy, Austria, Hungary, Bohemia, and Flanders. But there was considerable weakness in this large empire. The Spanish Habsburgs were still powerful, but decaying and inefficient. The Austrian House was weak, beset by hesitant rulers and the incessant war with the Turks. France was Catholic, having solved its Huguenot troubles; she was also strongly anti-Spanish. But her king, Henri IV, was killed in 1610, and Marie de Medicis ruled as regent. The real power behind the throne throughout the entire span of the Thirty Years' War was Cardinal Richelieu, but weakened by internal conflict and intrigue, France was not in a position to oppose Spain openly until well into the 1630's. In the meantime she formed protective alliances with some of the German states and Sweden, many of them Protestant powers. This religious war was, after all, not all about religion!

And then, the inevitable incidents occurred. On May 23, 1618, the Protestant nobility of Bohemia revolted and threw the Catholic ministers, the allies of Spain, out of the windows of Hradcany Castle and declared their independence from the Habsburgs. The "Defenestration of Prague," as this act is officially called, had dire consequences. Two years later, after the Czechs lost their battles, Protestant heads were rolling on Old Town Square.

Further incidents followed in Germany, in the Valtelline, in the Palatinate. The alliances and protective leagues set their awesome machinery in motion. For a while France persuaded the two German leagues, the Catholic League and the Evangelical Union, to remain neutral, but this did not last long. A general war ensued. Was it really the result of an inexorable march of events? Perhaps it was, but Trevor-Roper[8] believes that Spain's decision made it happen. Full control over the whole Continent coupled with her colonial empire seemed to be in her grasp. As it turned out, the familiar fate of great nations befell her; the Peace of Westphalia put an end to Spain as a great power.

War followed war within the next thirty years. It is somewhat arbitrarily separated into individual conflicts, and one develops a sense of proportion about their complexity from the roll call of long-forgotten battles and places. The Bohemian and Palatine War lasted from 1618 to 1623; the Fights for the Graubünden, from 1620 to 1639. This hotly contested border between Italy and the Tyrol included one of the original hot spots, the Valtelline, essential for the control of travel between Italy and Southern Germany. The Swedish-Polish War was from 1621 to 1629, and the Danish War, from 1625 to 1629. The War of the Mantuan Succession (1628-1631) was hardly more than a pretext to start the active war between France and Spain. The Swedish War (1630-1635) introduced one of the most important events of the Thirty Years' War, the involvement of Gustavus Adolphus's army in Germany. One of the most fantastic plans, frequently but incorrectly called the War of Smolensk (1632-1634), consisted of a loose, abortive, and hopeless alliance between Gustavus Adolphus, Cardinal Richelieu, Prince Gabor Bethlen of Transylvania, and some Russian forces, mostly Ukranian cossacks, against the Imperial Armies of the Austrian Habsburgs and Poland. In the end, there was the French and Swedish War (1635-1648) and the Swedish-Danish War (1643-1645).

The strategy and tactics of these campaigns is fascinating, but beyond the scope of this book. During the first ten years, the Habsburgs and the Catholic alliance were victorious. Then, their luck changed. The Swedes turned the tide in 1631 at the battle of Breitenfels. These struggles brought two great generals to the fore, Albrecht von Wallenstein, the commander of the Imperial Forces, and Gustavus Adolphus, King of Sweden. They fought each other in some of the greatest battles of the war. After a few years, having revolutionized the conduct of war, they both met violent ends. Gustavus Adolphus was killed in the battle of Lützen in 1632; Wallenstein, charged with treason, was assassinated two years later. The tide of Protestant victory declined after Gustavus's death, and so did the morale and discipline of the so far unbeatable Swedish army. After the death of the two great commanders, purposeful war came to an end even in the main theater of the Thirty Years' War, Germany. The various commanders, Swedish, Bavarian, French, and Imperial, waged war on their own, without coherent pattern or strategy. The campaign degenerated into raids and skirmishes.

Finally, peace came in form of the treaties signed in Westphalia in 1648. The settlements favored Sweden, France, and
some of their German allies. Spain was finished as a territorial
power. Most of the German states gained little but a religious
equality of rights for being the main battle ground for decades.
The Austrian Habsburg dynasty survived, but their claim to the
Holy Roman Empire became an empty gesture.

This, then, was the large picture. How did it look to the men
in the armies?

Battles of many wars were described in detail at all levels of
participation, but an account of a battle in the sixteenth or seventeenth century by a fighting man who also possessed literary
skill was by no means common. Grimmelshausen gave a vivid account of an engagement between his unit, a troup of Imperial
dragoons and a squadron of Swedish cavalry in the battle of
Wittstock, on September 24, 1636. An etching of Callot serves
as its pictorial counterpart (Fig. 5).

"Within seconds the air was filled with whining bullets . . .
those who were timid ducked as if they could hide; those with

Figure 5. Detail from Callot's "Cavalry Encounter."

more courage kept their wits and let the bullets fly overhead without batting an eyelid; in the engagement that followed everybody sought death by killing the first man encountered. The gruesome sound of shooting, the clashing of steel, the cracking of pikes, the yelling of both attackers and wounded, added to the sound of trumpets, drums, and fifes, made a horrible music. Nothing could be seen but smoke and dust which appeared to cover the wounded and the dead; out of this cloud came the pitiful cries of the dying and the lusty yells of those still fighting; even the horses became excited the longer they defended their masters, covered with foam, some falling to the ground dead under their riders, covered by wounds—unjust reward for their faithful service; others fell on their riders, receiving in death the honor of being carried by those whom they themselves had to carry while still alive; again others, having unburdened themselves of their masters, left them behind in their rage and frenzy and bolted, seeking freedom in far away fields. The earth itself, accustomed to cover the dead was now covered by bodies, slain in different ways; heads lay where their owners lost them, elsewhere were bodies without a head; some displayed their bowels in a horrible and pitiful way; the heads of others were shattered with their brain splashed around; some could be seen loosing the blood from their soulless body while others were splattered with the lifeblood of strangers; here an arm cut off with fingers still moving as if to return to fight while others fled without having lost a drop of blood; legs torn from the body and grown heavier than they were before although unburdened by the weight of the body they used to carry. Mutilated soldiers asking to be killed while others are begging for mercy: Summa summarum, nothing but a miserable, pitiful sight!"

Chapter 3

THE SOLDIERS

◇◇◇

*T*HE soldiers were a real hodgepodge of every nation of the European continent: Imperial troups of the Holy Roman Empire, many of them Austrians, then Bavarians, Hessians, Swabians, and natives of all the kingdoms and duchies of Germany; and the Swedish troups of Gustavus Adolphus, French, Spaniards, Vallons, Poles, Croats, and adventurers from England and Scotland. While these latter countries did not participate in the war, many of their sons served as officers with the belligerents, mostly in Gustavus Adolphus's army. They also fought under the Imperial flag; the former commander-in-chief of the Imperial forces, Wallenstein, was murdered by his Irish, English, and Scot officers. Some of the soldiers were professionals; others were pressed into service, and many were mercenaries. These latter were still generally referred to as Landsknechts, or Lansquenets in the French corruption of the term. The first Landsknechts were German and Swiss mercenary foot soldiers in the sixteenth century, their name originally meaning "man of the plains." By the time of the Thirty Years' War, they served in various forces, but remained predominantly German.

The common soldier's life was harsh. In his *Simplicissimus,* Grimmelshausen gives his own account: "Some (soldiers) were lustier than others but they were generally defiant, overbearing, mostly godless, yet usually carrying a heavy, sometimes unbearable burden, expressed in such rhymes:

> Hunger und Durst, auch Hitz und Kält,
> Arbeit und Armut, wie es fällt,
> Gewalttat, Ungerechtigheit,
> Treiben wir Landsknecht allezeit.

> (Hunger and thirst, heat and cold,
> Toil and poverty, as it comes,
> Violence and injustice
> Drives us Landsknechts all the time.)

20

". . . to devour and to booze, to hunger and to thirst, to wench and to pimp, to play and throw dice, to feast and to revel, to murder and be murdered, to kill and be killed, to torture and be tortured, to hunt and be hunted, to strike terror and be terrorized, to rob and be robbed, to plunder and be plundered, to scare and be scared, to torment and suffer, to beat and be beaten; in a word, to hurt and to harm and in turn being hurt and harmed, this was their whole life."

"Until after all the fights, battles, skirmishes and sieges they died, perished and croaked; except for those few who have stolen and plundered enough or who in their advanced age became the very best beggars and tramps."

There were, of course, commanders who cared about their men. Condottieris and captains of mercenary troops were eager to maintain the fighting quality of their troops since their power, including the bargaining power to sell their services to the highest bidder, depended to a great extent on the fitness of their men and their willingness to fight. Their soldiers were professionals rewarded mostly by the loot. When dissatisfied with either treatment or loot, they mutinied or changed sides, sometimes in the middle of a battle. Many a captain ended his career by being stabbed in the back or hacked to pieces by his own men.

The regular armies were regular only in a manner of speaking. Many of the soldiers were conscripts, in other words pressed into service by recruiting and press gangs; these unfortunates had no professional military skill to start with and had to suffer the full brunt of inhuman treatment. They were expendable, and they knew it. Most of their commanders made no bones about it. Paré quotes Emperor Charles V of Spain on the heavy casualties inflicted upon his soldiers: "He said then that it did not matter if they did die, comparing them to caterpillars, grasshoppers and cockchafers which eat the buds and other good things of earth, saying that if they were men of worth they would not be in his camp at six livres a month; therefore no harm was done if they did die."[9] The view of the common soldier's worthlessness was slow to change. Three hundred years later the Duke of Wellington said of his men who served him so well at Waterloo: "They are the scum of the earth. All English soldiers are fellows who enlisted for drink."

If commanders in the field felt like this, leaders of states cared even less. As Robert Burton wrote in his *Anatomy of Melancholy* in 1621: The battles are bloody; thousands are slain at once, while statesmen, secure at home, "take their ease and follow their lusts, not considering what intolerable misery poor soldiers endure, their often wounds, hunger and thirst. . . ."[10]

At the same time the first vestiges of army organization as we know it came into being. The troops were raised by colonels, to whom the Emperor issued recruiting commissions. The military system was organized on a regimental basis with the various ranks and their duties clearly defined. Actually, it was the Thirty Years' War that blunted the sharp difference between various categories of soldiers of the previous centuries. As Clausewitz[11] pointed out, the feudal levies were first transformed into mercenaries. But these armies of mercenaries did not last long. When the soldier, hired for a limited term, was turned into a standing mercenary, the military force became a standing army, supported regularly (at least in theory) by the state.

The gap separating the officers from the common soldiers was very wide, and most officers received their commission because of noble birth. However, it became possible to raise from the ranks. The wisdom of this was hotly debated.

Grimmelshausen, himself a man who rose from the ranks, construed a dialogue between Adelhold, obviously a nobleman, and a sergeant to give the arguments of both sides: "Tell me, old grouch," asked Adelhold, "are officers of noble birth not more respected by common soldiers than those who were farm-hands before? And should not a commander in the field trust a knight more than a peasant boy who enlisted for the sole reason of abandoning his father's plow? A true nobleman would rather die than dishonor himself through cowardice or treason. . . . In addition, nobility has the means to finance its troops and supply weak companies with men. . . . It ill behooves to place a peasant over a nobleman in rank; the former might become arrogant when made into a master:

Es ist kein Schwert das schärfer schiert,
Als wenn ein Baur zum Herren wird.

"No sword cuts sharper than
A peasant who is made lord."

The sergeant answered: "What fool would serve without a hope to advance in rank through good behavior and be rewarded for faithful service? The devil take such a war! This way it does not matter whether one fights well or not. I often heard our old colonel say that he would not tolerate any soldier in his regiment who does not sincerely believe that through good performance he could become a general. It is known all over the world that those nations who reward the bravery of the common soldier, are usually victorious, as seen by the example of the Persians and Turks."

"This is true," said Adelhold, ". . . and one finds many today who abandoned the plow, the sewing needle, the cobbler's awl and exchanged the shepherd's stick with the sword to become not only noblemen but barons and counts through faithful service and bravery."

"This all sounds very nice." answered the sergeant, "but I still see it all too clearly that for us the doors leading to any position of dignity are kept closed by the nobility."

So, the soldier's life remained grim, and the end, all too predictable. Who could forget the scene of Paré's first experience in military surgery as he witnessed in mute horror as an old soldier cut the throats of his mortally wounded comrades as a last act of mercy? Many of the surgeons were truly considerate to these poor brutes of men. The kindness of Ambroise Paré shines through the pages of his case histories; neither was Scultetus lacking in compassion.

Chapter 4

THE WEAPONS

*I*N earlier times, hand-to-hand combat was the essence of the battle, and an arresting blow to the head was the quickest way to dispose of the opponent. And arresting they were! Courville[12] examined the skulls from one of the Hussite battles, fought in the vicinity of Kutna Hora, in Bohemia in the fifteenth century. Many skeletons, particularly the skulls, are preserved to the present day in the nearby chapel and ossuary, arranged in decorative garlands as a grisly "memento mori." These skeletal remains, as well as the bodies exhumed from the mass graves of the earlier (1361) battle of Wisby in Gotland, gave mute evidence.[13, 14] Roughly one half of all skulls showed severe, possibly lethal damage. The evidence included signs of contusion of the bone, linear fractures or defects inflicted by the broadsword and round perforations from bolts of the crossbow or pikes. Most of them were depressed fractures of various shapes and sizes, the result of blows by clubs, maces, and pole-arms. Up to the early sixteenth century, the professional soldiers fought with halberds, pikes, and other pole-arms, battle-axes, swords, and maces. The long range weapon was, of course, the bow and arrow and the crossbow, an accurate and deadly weapon with a high power of penetration.[15] Peasant armies largely improvized and turned their tools of the field into arms. They were equally terrible at close range, the pitchforks, spiked flails, home-made pikes, and the straightened scythes. They remained the weapons of the oppressed for a long time to come. As late as 1848, in the earliest battles of the Hungarian revolution against the Habsburgs when rifles were scarce, the insurgents routed Imperial troops with straightened scythes.

By the time of the Thirty Years' War, military tactics changed with the use of firearms. Close combat remained, as it always will, the realm of the foot soldier. Artillery came into its own,

24

particularly in beseiging fortifications and as the opening salvo of major engagements, but was little used in the skirmishes and pitched battles which characterized this war with the exception of the Swedish artillery of Gustavus Adolphus. His four-pounders were light, highly mobile, and could be discharged faster than the volleys of the best infantry.

Muskets, arquebuses, and pistols were commonly used, although they were cumbersome, inaccurate, and short-ranged. They inflicted injuries to the head, of course, but other parts of the body were more often damaged since accurate aim was hardly possible, and the torso and limbs offered a larger target than the head. Consequently, head injuries remained within the realm of close-combat weapons. Most of the cases described by Scultetus were injured by swords and clubs, although otherwise bullet wounds were frequent, and he describes a variety of special instruments for their removal (Fig. 6).

Almost a hundred years earlier, the records of Ambroise Paré give evidence to the frequency of bullet wounds: "I visited a great number of Gentlemen and poor soldiers, and among others, many Swiss Captains. I dressed fourteen of them in a single room, all wounded with shots of pistols and other diabolical firearms."[16] The importance of these firearms prompted Paré to publish his famous treatise, "The Method of Treating Wounds Made by Harquebuses and Other Fire-Arms," as early as 1545.[17]

Firearms were frequently referred to as diabolical. This epithet had considerable meaning: Since gunpowder was made of the devil's stuff, sulphur, saltpeter, and charcoal, the resulting explosion could only be diabolical. It was also thought that devils rode on the bullets, which explains why bullet wounds were believed to be poisonous. Arrows, on the other hand, with feathers on their shafts resembling angels' wings, were more acceptable if not necessarily angelic.

What were these diabolical firearms like? The early matchlock muskets were heavy and cumbersome, some between five and six feet in length and weighing over twelve pounds. About the end of the sixteenth century, the wheel lock was invented;

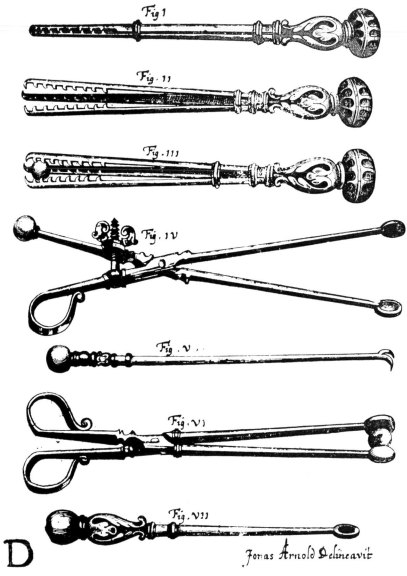

Figure 6. Scultetus' instruments for the removal of bullets ("ad globulos sclopetorum e vulneribus trahendos").

it reached the height of its development during the seventeenth century.[18] The wheel lock was the standard firing mechanism of the muskets used in the Thirty Years' War, although the more primitive match-lock muskets were still used. The stocks of wheel-lock guns were usually straight and very short. It was placed on a forked rest before aiming and firing, and considerable difficulty would have been experienced had a quick shot from the shoulder been necessary. When used in battle by mounted men, they were presumedly fired from either the hip or the thigh.[18] However, there is evidence of their being fired from the shoulder as seen in dramatic detail in Jacques Callot's engraving of "Attack on the Highway" (Fig. 7).

Many passages in *Simplicissimus* prove that Grimmelshausen indeed served as a musketeer during the war. He was familiar with its use and described in great detail how an experienced sol-

Figure 7. Detail from Jacques Callot's "Attack on the Highway," showing the handling of the musket at close range. (Courtesy Prints Division, The New York Public Library, Astor, Lennox and Tilden Foundations and *Horizon Magazine*.)

dier keeps lock, pan, and powder dry in rainy weather. These muskets did not fire when wet. The other hazard was premature ignition with the flames carried on to the many pouches of powder hanging from bandoliers across the poor soldier's chest and resulting in fearful burns. They were cumbersome and inaccurate weapons; seasoned riflemen stood their ground and did not fire until they saw the white of the enemies' eyes, a rule mentioned by Grimmelshausen and still valid in the battle of Bunker Hill 150 years later (Fig. 8).

Neither were pistols more accurate, although they were in great demand. The usual length of the barrel was about a foot; the length of the whole pistol with its stock, about a foot and one-half. They were also wheel-lock operated, although an advanced design, the so-called snaphaunce-lock, made its appearance toward the end of the war, mostly among Scottish soldiers of fortune.[18] The snaphaunce pistols were lighter with a shorter barrel, but singularly inaccurate at any but close range. The muzzle velocity of all these pistols was low. In the middle of the seventeenth century, "the bullet sized to the bore is five lignes in diameter, the charge a dram of powder, and it will carry forty paces, more or less, according to the goodness of the powder."[19]

No wonder, then, that head injuries suffered from these large, slow-flying projectiles resulted in a depressed skull fracture rather than in a deep, penetrating missile wound. Grimmelshausen described an incident when a soldier fired his pistol at the forehead of a peasant at close range. This had "as much effect as if it would have hit a steel mountain" (whereafter the soldier, greatly upset by this fiasco, yelled: "Since you do not want to go to heaven, I send you to the kingdom of hell" and split his opponents head in half with his sword "down to his teeth"). In this respect, the old-fashioned crossbow was superior not only in accuracy of aim, but also in impact. The bolts were much narrower in diameter than bullets and punctured the skull neatly.

Not all soldiers were armed with firearms, even in professional armies. Sometimes less than one fifth of the troops carried guns or pistols. Earlier, the average soldier was a "pike-man."

Figure 8. Musketeer of the early seventeenth century, by W. de Ghein. Steel helmet was sometimes worn under the wide brimmed hat. The leather pouches attached to the bandolier contained measured amount of gunpowder. (From "Warriors and Worthies." Courtesy Helmut Nickel and The Metropolitan Museum of Art).

Landsknechts of the sixteenth century used pikes. It is because of the "lange Spiess" (long pike or lance), the typical weapon with which they were armed, that the name "lansquenet" in French, "lanzknecht" in German, and "lance-knight" in English came into use. The pike, a common form of infantry spear, had a small diamond-shaped steel head on a long staff, made of the wood of ash, aspen, or pine. In the sixteenth and seventeenth centuries, most regiments consisted of pike-men as well as musketeers, the former serving to keep the cavalry away from the latter. Various combinations of "shot and pike" were used. The pike-men stood four or five deep and, with their weapons thrust forward through their own ranks, formed an impenetrable hedge (Fig. 9). Although the pike survived well beyond the seventeenth century, Sir James Turner, writing in his *Pallas Armata* in 1670, already decided that the pike, "the Prince of Weapons," was falling into disuse.[20] By the time of the Thirty Years' War, most professional soldiers and particularly high-quality mercenaries were equipped with firearms. Their fighting value and life, short as it was, depended on the excellence of their weapons. Musketeers represented the elite of the infantry; pike-men, its lowest class.

Cavalry tactics changed from previous wars. Heavily armored horsemen were replaced by light cavalry used for shock effect with pistol and saber in pitched battles and hit-and-run attacks on convoys and encampments. The Swedish army organized the first corps of dragoons, cavalry equipped with both sabers and muskets, and able to fight both mounted and unmounted. The other armies followed suit. Grimmelshausen himself was a dragoon in the Imperial Army. The equipment and deployment of these mounted troops set a pattern that did not change much until the First World War.

Defensive weapons included many types of light armor, cuirasses and half-cuirasses covering the chest. However, the use of body armor declined for sake of mobility. Gustavus Adolphus himself wore only a leather buff coat, no protection against the pistol shots that killed him in the battle of Lützen in 1632.[21] The head was usually protected by helmet. They were as heavy, hot, and bothersome as they are now.

Figure 9. Pikeman facing cavalry charge, by W. de Ghein, 1608.

Marauding soldiers and peasant bands used whatever weapon came handy. However, it would be a mistake to believe that enraged peasants fought only with their bare hands. Many of those who organized themselves into guerilla bands and attacked small units of soldiers and stragglers were armed with weapons from their victims. Grimmelshausen mentioned this on several occasions quite matter-of-factly and described a grim fight between Croatian musketeers and peasants, many of whom were armed with "fire-locks."

Chapter 5

THE SURGEONS

*W*HAT were they like? Some were learned physicians, innovators in theory and practice. Others remained ignorant, illiterate barbers. Napoleon's maxim that every soldier carries the marshall's baton in his knapsack was true in the sixteenth through seventeenth centuries, but few soldiers became marshalls, and few surgeons achieved fame. There were, of course, exceptions.

Giacomo Berengario da Carpi (1470-1550) became one of the most prominent anatomists before Vesalius and managed to combine a busy and lucrative practice with investigative work. Although professor at Bologna for twenty years, he traveled widely all over Italy for practice and pleasure, a true renaissance man, friend of famous people and artists. He wrote a book on head injuries after he cured Lorenzo de Medici, duke of Urbino, from a wound of the head received in battle. While in Rome, he introduced Benvenuto Cellini and some of his designs and silverwork to the Pope. One of the chapters of Cellini's autobiography is entirely devoted to "Maestro Giacomo Berengario da Carpi . . . a surgeon of the highest renown." "He only undertook a cure after stipulating for his fees, which he reckoned not by tens, but by hundreds of crowns. He was a great connoisseur in the arts of design." He also cunningly carried away Cellini's drawings with him on his departure from Rome. This departure was hurried. "He was a person of great sagacity, and did wisely to get out of Rome; for not many months afterwards, all the patients he treated (mostly for syphilis, with mercury) grew so ill that they were a hundred times worse off than before they came. He would certainly have been murdered if he had stopped."

A few years later Ambroise Paré, who was poorly educated, started out as a military surgeon and became surgeon to four successive kings of France, beginning with Henri II. Eventually he became "Premier Chirugien" and "Conseilleur du Roi." More than that, through a combination of surgical skill, experience, boldness, and keen observation he became, more than any other man, the founder of modern surgery.

Scultetus' mentor, Hieronymus Fabricius ab Aquapendente (1537-1619), was not only an ingenious surgeon, but one of the greatest of all teachers of anatomy. He succeeded Fallopius and built, at his own expense, the anatomical theatre at Padua where he became professor of surgery. So widespread was his reputation that even tailors, cobblers, butchers, and shopkeepers wanted to watch him dissecting. He had many disciples from all over Europe, among them Scultetus who payed tribute to his mentor in many pages of his book. Among his many claims to fame, one of the greatest is that he taught Harvey. It is almost certain that the discovery of circulation by Harvey was promoted by the observation of Fabricius ab Aquapendente that the venous valves faced toward the heart and prevented the flow of blood away from it.

A famous contemporary of Scultetus in Germany was Wilhelm Fabry von Hilden, or as he was most frequently referred to, Fabricius Hildanus (1560-1624). Orphaned at a young age and having survived the bubonic plague, he became a barber surgeon's apprentice. He was lucky because he served for twelve years under several quite distinguished wound-surgeons, including Jean Griffon of Geneva, one of the best barber surgeons of the age. He also became acquainted with physicians who were educated in Italy. As a result he not only developed into a competent and imaginative surgeon, but also into an innovator and writer of considerable merit. Fabricius Hildanus was well educated in the humanities, and spoke and wrote Latin. He was a busy and very successful practitioner of the healing arts, and his reputation spread beyond the borders of Germany. Strangely enough for those times, he was married to a woman who was also highly esteemed as a surgeon and midwife and who assisted him in his work.

Scultetus himself was obviously well trained. He was a physician, not a barber, who spoke Latin and Greek and obtained his training in Padua, the foremost center of surgical learning of the time. He was one of the most enterprising and venturesome surgeons of his era and well known at the time of his death at the age of fifty. One wonders, however, whether his name would be even remembered if he would not have written his masterpiece, the *Armamentarium Chirurgicum*, his only known treatise.

There was a tremendous abyss between these men of learning and the barber surgeons. Between the doctors and the barbers there existed another class of surgeons whom we might call educated barber surgeons because they had some formal training and took courses at the universities. Among these relatively few belongs Ambroise Paré who became master-surgeon and surgeon to the king, although he was essentially self-taught and never mastered Latin, a serious social flaw among professionals of the time.

The ordinary barber surgeon's life was not easy. Hamby[9] gives a graphic description of what it was like: "Those who aspired to be licensed as barber surgeons were not educated people. They served apprenticeships under barber surgeons, and their lives were hard ones. They slaved in the barber shops, shaving patrons, trimming beards, clipping hair, dressing wigs, and assisting their masters in their crude surgery. Their masters were not eager to have these potential competitors learn much or progress rapidly; they were kept at their menial tasks as rigorously as possible. Apprentices with ambition, intelligence and energy to learn and to progress in surgery had few literary resources. Unable to read Latin, they had to depend upon word-of-mouth instruction and whatever French translations of earlier authors were available to them."

There were many complaints to higher authorities when such existed. The Barber-Surgeons Company in England maintained a court, mostly to deal with disciplinary problems, but also with grievances. Still on record are complaints of apprentices for "being beaten by the master unreasonably" and "not being given sufficient meat and drink." Perhaps marrying into a well-established barber surgeon family was one of the easier ways to ascend. This must have been common practice since there are on record many barber surgeon families of several generations.

It would be a mistake to believe that all barber surgeons were downtrodden pariahs of the medical profession. Some became not only skillful surgeons, but powerful men to reckon with. Many were men of dignity and conscience. "It is the office of the surgeon to unite with his hand that of man's body which has been separated or which is open and make it into a whole as it had been before, wherever possible," wrote Hieronymus Brunschwig in his *Cirurgia* (1497). Another barber surgeon, Hans von Gersdorff proudly declared: "The surgeon distinguishes himself from the physician in that the physician does no manual work . . . it is necessary that the surgeon have good intelligence and understanding. Not too rash in his actions, but always well aware of the harm that might come to him or to the patient because of his lack of skill" (*Das Feldbuch der Wundarzney,* 1517).[1]

The status of the barber surgeons depended to a great extent on the educational and social background of their respective countries. In England and in France, with their somewhat fossilized university structures and medical systems, their lot was hard. In Italy, easygoing then as now, they were tolerated and got along with the university-trained physicians, and were even thought to be indispensable as craftsmen of the trade. In Germany, slowly and uncertainly emerging from the Middle Ages, they flourished. They might have been tolerated and therefore timid in other countries; in Germany they were robust. Felix Wirtz (1510-1580), while officially a "Scherer" (barber), had the courage to say: "What do you suppose I care whether Galen's or Avicenna's or Guy de Chauliac's opinion does or does not agree with mine?"[22]

In some countries, particularly in England and France, serious efforts were made to organize the barbers and insist on examination and licensure to maintain standards of proficiency. Itinerant quacks were the bane of the profession. The extent of the problem they represented can be fully appreciated from a proclamation of Henry VIII in 1512 which prohibits "craftsmen, women, sorcerers, weavers, and smiths" to perform surgery. Not much better were the wandering lithotomists who cut stones, set fractures, etc. in courtyards, at fairs, and wherever they could get hold of a patient. However, "legitimate" barbers were not much better thought of. Norman Dott[23] quotes Maister Peter Lowe, founder of the Royal College of Physicians and Surgeons in Glasgow, in 1599 as saying: "Barbers and other ignorant fellows . . . being most arrogant . . . take upon them to cure and heal every disease . . . by which they ruin infinite number of people."[24]

Except for rare instances, initial treatment of head injuries was given by barbers. Sixteen of the "Observations" in the book of Scultetus include the description of what could be called first aid or initial treatment. Afterwards, usually days later, Scultetus was called into consultation or took over the management of the patient. Ten of the patients were seen by physicians, fellow surgeons, or military surgeons, some of them "young and inexperienced." An exception was the "learned and distinguished colleague, Joannis Georgius Gockelius, doctor of philosophy and medicine and appointed physician to the Republic (city) of Ulm." Most of the other patients were treated, at least initially, by barber surgeons. These "common barber surgeons" (barbitonsores vulgares) were a constant source of vexation to Scultetus who does not even attempt to mask his contempt for them. Statements such as ". . . a certain barber surgeon called Villanus now started to treat his head injury, the treatment of which he did not have the slightest notion about . . ." are common. One patient was taken to a bath-keeper (Balneator), with predictable result. "It is therefore suggested to the Senate of the Republic of Ulm," wrote Scultetus, "that barber surgeons should not be allowed to treat head injuries of serious nature or to treat such injuries in patients who are in a half-dead condition within the community of Ulm."

He was sometimes critical about the quality of treatment rendered by fellow physicians. Ulm was a provincial backwater compared with Padua, and methods were crude. His training in Italy and the longing for a more sophisticated professional en-

vironment shows in several passages of the *Armamentarium:*
"This operation [perforation of the skull] is carried out frequently in Italy; it is rather rare in the territory of Ulm and the
neglect of such cases is regrettable." Certain technical details
"should be fully observed by surgeons in Germany where such
surgical operations are less customary than in Italy or France."

Consultations were frequently called for; they were quite customary in the time of Ambroise Paré. Hamby[9] thought that
the reason for this was not so much the lack of self-assurance
on the surgeon's part, but rather the penalty for failure without
adequate sharing of responsibility. This is stated quite clearly
by Scultetus, who was frequently called into such consiliums.
"On the tenth day, the parents of the patient requested a consultation," that involved three physicians (Obs. XV). The matter of "informed consent" must have also plagued the surgeons
of his era: "The learned and well disposed surgeon should tell
the patient and point out the danger of the operation." "The
surgeon in such a case [when trepanation is necessary] should
immediately make a statement in which he predicts the danger
to the patient's life, to avoid stupid gossip by laymen."

Clearly, one had to be on guard against unpleasant consequences. A patient of the distinguished Doctor Gockelius who
"showed no evidence of severe injury nor skull fracture, not to
mention depression in the skull" and who was treated "with all
appropriate internal and external medication," nevertheless died
of a brain abscess which was found at autopsy. In no time at
all, Doctor Gockelius was in trouble: "Here now begins the cal-
vary of my distinguished colleague since he has been asked nu-
merous questions by the prefects of Ulm, whether he incised
the wound and dilated the edges, inspected the bone and considered trephination or not." A familiar note from the distant
past!

One of the main problems was, of course, that the treatment
of injuries, and head injuries in particular, underwent major
changes during the sixteenth and early seventeenth centuries under the influence gained in the wars. Much of what was new
contradicted established authorities to whom some lip service

was still paid. In some ways the general treatment of wounds was not as sound as it could have been. Wounds were treated by open methods, salves, and "digestive ointments," although an effort was made to sew up large defects and gaping wounds. This represented a curious opposition to the thirteenth and early fourteenth centuries when many surgeons, particularly those trained in Bologna, advocated closure by primary suture. Their spokesman, Henri de Mondeville, openly stated that it is not only unnecessary but harmful to generate pus and that the wound should simply be cleaned with wine, the edges brought together with stitches, and left for nature to heal. Bruno da Longoburgo spoke, for the first time, of healing by "first and second intention." Unfortunately, this progress was interrupted in the middle of the fourteenth century by Guy de Chauliac whose influence was felt for centuries to come. He abandoned the antiseptic treatment of wounds and returned to ointments and to the promotion of the "pus laudabile" of Galen. By the sixteenth and seventeenth centuries surgeons were still uncertain about the value of this dogma. Ambroise Paré seemed to be inclined to suture grossly dehiscent wounds; Scultetus was more in favor of open management.

In spite of his flair for superstition, Matthäus Gottfried Purmann (1648-1721) was a very experienced and skillful surgeon. He was the first among surgeons who at the end of the seventeenth century raised the question: Is it necessary to bring wounds to suppuration "according to Ancient Custom"? He found evidence to the contrary and disposed of the concept of "laudable pus." "I soon found it true, that wounds might be constantly and perfectly cured without Suppuration, or the Application of Plaisters, Balsams, Oyls, Ointments, and such like nasty greasie Medicines, which under Pretence of suppurating, Mundifying and keeping the Wound Open for some time; the Lips, Edges, and the Flesh were corrupted, by imbibing those greasie Drugs, and made more painful, by keeping it open; not to mention other ill Accidents, that too often happen while you are waiting for a suppuration."[1]

Whatever their principle of wound healing, these learned surgeons must have reflected the thoughts of John of Mirfield, physician and hospital chaplain of the late fourteenth century: "Each (medical) man should know that he will not be a good physician who does not know the basic practice of surgery. And on the other hand, a surgeon who does not know medicine ought to be considered worthless."[25]

The main source of Scultetus' knowledge was his training with Fabricius ab Aquapendente and his practical experience as military and municipal surgeon during the Thirty Years' War. In his *Armamentarium* he mentioned Galen and Celsus—mostly to prove his erudition rather than for practical purposes. He attributed some of the principles in the treatment of head injuries to Guy de Chauliac (c1300-1368), "le bon Guidon" of Ambroise Paré, still revered after centuries. His *La Grand Chirurgie*, published in Lyon in 1478, was still read. In addition, there were many abbreviated editions written in the vernacular rather than in Latin to be more easily understood by poorly educated students and barbers. These little guides, the "petit guydon," were among the most popular books of medical literature, and hardly any surgeon or barber could be found without one in his pocket or saddle bag. Since the name "Guy" and the word "guide" stem from the same root, the terms became synonymous. They were quite obsolete by the midseventeenth century, but still popular. So was Berengario da Carpi, or Berengarius, whose treatise on skull fractures, *Tractatus de Fractura Calve sive Cranei,* published in Bologna in 1518 with many subsequent editions, was an important source of reference. Closer in time was the book of Ambroise Paré on head injuries, *La Methode Curative des Playes et Fractures de la Teste Humain.* Written at the request of the King's physician, Chapelain, after the fatal head wound of Henri II, this book was published in Paris in 1562.[9] It was popular throughout the next century.

Most influential and most quoted by Scultetus were his contemporaries, Fabricius ab Aquapendente and Fabricius Hildanus. The *Opera Chirurgica in Duos Partes divisa* of Fabricius ab Aquapendente was printed in 1617, in Padua. The first part of this book, the "Surgical Pentateuch" was published separately in 1592. It dealt with tumors, ulcers, etc., and their surgical treatment. The second part, the "Surgical Operations" covered any known and many original surgical interventions from head to heel ("a capite ad calcem").

As far as Fabricius Hildanus is concerned, Scultetus must have been personally acquainted with him. Hildanus published the first part of his *Observationum et Curationum Chirurgicum Centuria* in 1598. Later, at various time intervals, he published further collections of his case reports in series of one hundred each, totaling six hundred surgical cases in six volumes (1606-1641). Scultetus was very familiar with this work, although the final compilation of Hildanus's life work ("Wund-Artzney, Ganzes Werk, und aller Bücher, so viel deren vorhanden . . . ausz dem Lateinischen in das Teutsche übersetzt. . . .") was not printed until 1652, after the death of Scultetus.

Not only did these authors serve as a source of reference (readily acknowledged and duly quoted) to Scultetus, but they also helped him in organizing his material for the *Armamentarium Chirurgicum*. The first part of the book, dealing with the technique of surgical procedures from head to toe, follows the pattern set by Fabricius ab Aquapendente. The case histories or "Observations" of the second part were obviously influenced by Hildanus.

Chapter 6

THE SURGICAL INSTRUMENTS

◇◇

*M*ANY of Scultetus' instruments can be traced back to antiquity. Others were invented in the previous century by Berengario da Carpi and Ambroise Paré, both superb surgical technicians. Scultetus' teacher in Padua, Fabricius ab Aquapendente, as well as his contemporary, Fabricius Hildanus in Germany, were instrument designers of renown. In glossing over the pictures and descriptions of their tools one can plainly see the first forms of our instruments emerging, many of them but slightly changed by the intervening centuries.

Knives and forceps were simple, but quite modern in design. The needles were crude, large, and used by hand with flax-thread for suture material. The thread was waxed to slip through the tissue with ease. The periosteum was separated from the skull with a special instrument similar to a strong forceps (Fig. 10). However, this was rarely used, said Scultetus, because the pericranium can be easily removed with the nails of the thumb and index finger or with the handle of a scalpel. He preferred this technique, that was also recommended by Ambroise Paré: "As far as the nails of the fingers are concerned, when they are long enough they are safer to use than any of the instruments." Nevertheless, instruments similar to our periosteal elevators and called *raspatorium* were also used (presumably by surgeons with short fingernails) (Fig. 11). These were also handy to probe fissures of the skull penetrating "to unknown depths."

Free fragments of depressed fractures were removed with various tools, some of them especially designed for this purpose. One was called "a forceps with parrot beak to be used to elevate all fragments while at the same time preserving the dura which is depressed by fragments of the fracture" (Fig. 10). Another was named "the forceps with a vulture beak" from the shape

42

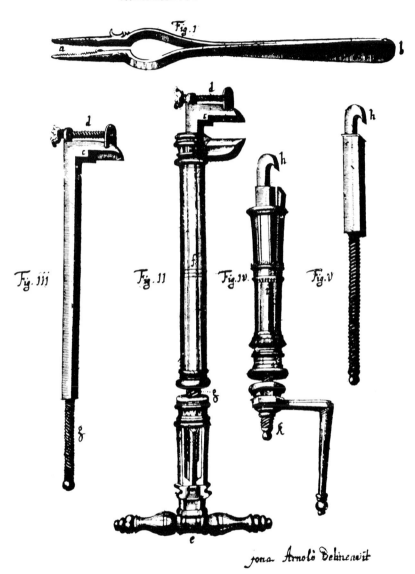

Figure 10. Forceps for the removal of the pericranium (I); instrument with parrot-beak (II, III); instrument with vulture-beak (IV, V).

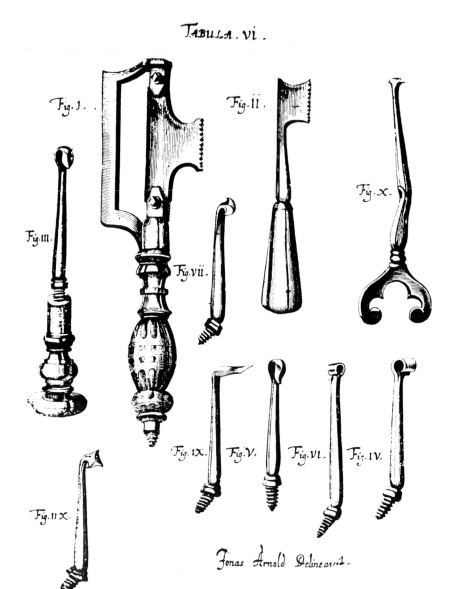

Figure 11. Bone saws, hook, elevators, and raspatoriums (periosteal elevators).

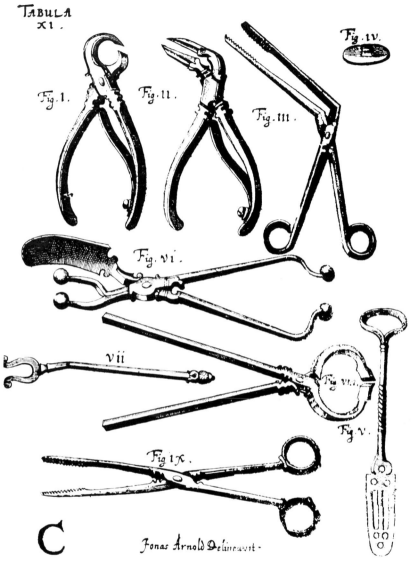

Figure 12. Rongeurs with parrot-beak and vulture-beak, used primarily for tooth extraction, but also for the removal of bone fragments in depressed skull fractures (I, II). Angled forceps identical in every detail with our Hartmann forceps (III).

of the lower lip of its biting edge (Fig. 10). They were remarkably similar in principle to our DeVilbiss cranial rongeur forceps, although in outward appearance they look more like monkey wrenches.

However, rongeurs similar to ours and called appropriately *parrot-beaked* and *vulture-beaked rongeurs* also appeared, and so did a remarkably true facsimile of our Hartmann forceps (Fig. 12). Although they were used mostly for dental work, Scultetus recommended their use for the removal of skull fragments. There were many dissectors available, including some resembling Penfield dissectors and the rather formidable looking elevator used by Ambroise Paré for lifting up severely depressed bone fragments (Fig. 13). A similar purpose was served by the lenticulus, a short and blunt knife with a round button at its tip (Fig. 14). The lenticulus was a favorite of Galen for the elevation and removal of depressed fractures and for other types of craniotomies. Its blunt end prevented "injury to the cerebral membranes during manipulation, also pain and inflammation. . . ."

One of the more esoteric contraptions was the three-legged terebra (terebra triploides or torcular) for the elevation of large, depressed portions of the skull (Fig. 13). This ingenious device was firmly placed on its three legs around the area to be operated upon, and its center screw was screwed into the middle of the depressed bone. The fragment pierced by the screw was then pulled to the surface, level with the adjacent bone edges, by a cogwheel mechanism. If necessary, the screw could be replaced by a rough-edged hook that could be inserted under the fragment through the fracture line. This was an old instrument, but still popular in the sixteenth and seventeenth centuries (Fig. 15). Despite its mechanical ingenuity, the tripod was not very effective. Scultetus pointed out its obvious shortcomings. Sometimes it separated the bone fragment and lifted out only the outer table. On other occasions, particularly when used by inexperienced men, the depressed bone was pushed further into the cranial cavity by trying to engage the center screw into the bone.

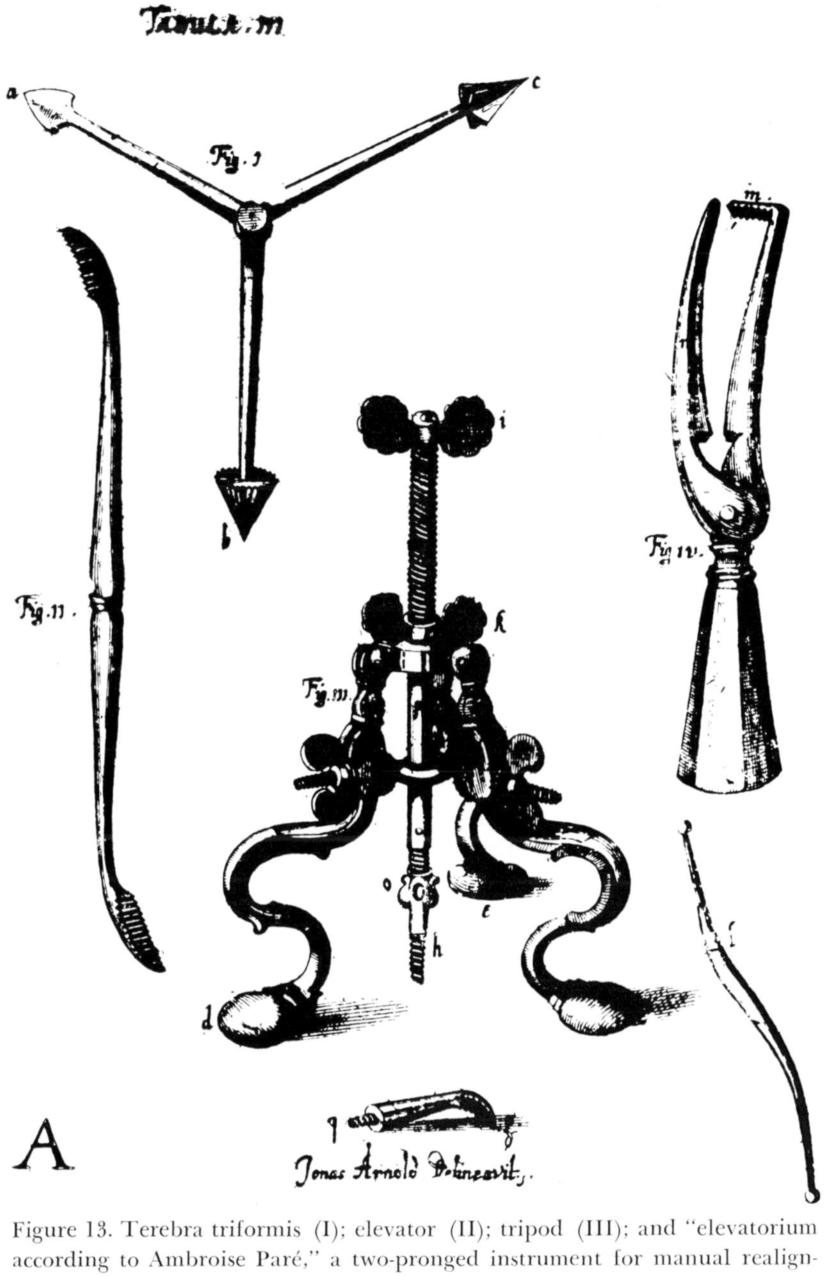

Figure 13. Terebra triformis (I); elevator (II); tripod (III); and "elevatorium according to Ambroise Paré," a two-pronged instrument for manual realignment of the fractured skull (IV).

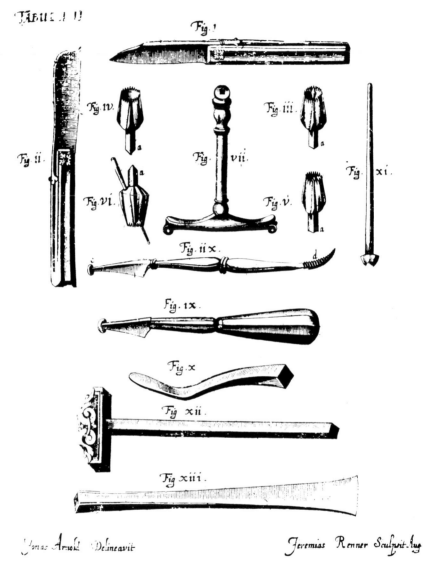

Figure 14. Surgical knives (I, II). "Modiolus with or without centerpin" (III-VII). It represents the final form of trephine used in our time without any further modification. Lenticulus (IIX, IX); malleable silver spatula (X); probe for depression of dura and for probing of epidural pus or hematoma, to be used separately or in conjunction with the modiolus (XI); lead-headed hammer and chisel used in craniotomies (XII, XIII).

It was the art of making a hole in the intact skull that taxed the ingenuity of our ancestors. No effort was spared to achieve this aim. The skull was drilled, chiseled, hacked, sawed, and gouged, and there were many instruments for this purpose. The basic instruments, dating back to antiquity and used with very little change in the seventeenth century, were the terebra or drill and the modiolus, a simple trephine.

The evolution of the classical instrument, the trepan, was described by Thompson.[26] To Fabricius ab Aquapendente, the mentor of Scultetus, is attributed the invention of the trephine, so-called for its triangular shape (Fig. 13). The reason for this name is its triangular form acquired by the horizontal position of the handle, in contradistinction to the trepan in which the head or crown is affixed to a frame or brace. The terebra serrata, or circular saw, of the ancients is described in detail by Scultetus, and his picture of this instrument is truly identical with the one we use these days (Fig. 14). He mentioned that before applying it to the skull one has to use the center pin so that the trephine is firmly applied. Scultetus described what he termed "male" and "female" trepan, the former having a center pin. "Before we use the females," he wrote, "we must make some print upon the skull with the male so that the females may stand the faster upon it." The trephine has to be turned around rapidly by its transverse handle, called the *manubrium* or *vertibulum*. Rapid rotation causes heat in the skull which in turn inflames the cerebral membranes. To counteract this, the trephine has to be dipped in cold water or rose oil.

This nomenclature is very confusing; although the Latin names of some of the instruments were used somewhat loosely in the old days, the subject is further obscured by our present-day terminology. An instrument ending in a drill point was generally called a *trephine*. What we call trephine, ending in a circular saw, was referred to as *terebra serrata* or *modiolus serratus*. The term *modiolus*, no longer used, was generally applied to instruments that made a hole in the skull by circumrotation.

To Fabricius ab Aquapendente is also attributed the invention of the circular saw with shoulders to prevent the instru-

Von den hauptwunden.

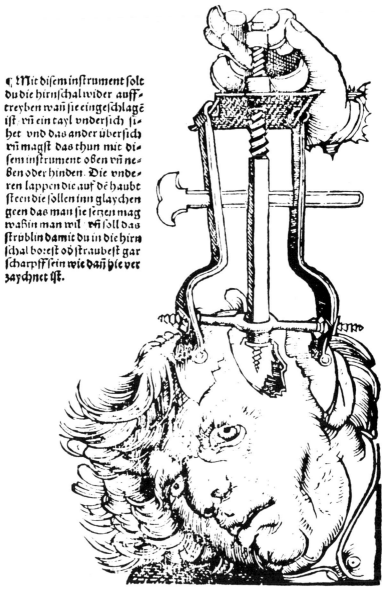

Mit disem instrument solt du die hirnschal wider auff-treyben wan sie eingeschlage ist vñ ein tayl vndersich si-het vnd das ander übersich vñ magst das thun mit di-sem instrument oben vñ ne-ben oder hinden. Die vnde-ren lappen die auf dē haubt steen die sollen inn glaychen geen das man sie setzen mag wahin man wil vñ soll das ströblin damit du in die hirn schal borest od straubest gar scharpff sein wie dañ hie ver zaychnet ist.

Figure 15. Elevation of depressed skull fragment with the torcular. From Hans von Gersdorff's "Feldtbuch der Wundartzney" (Fieldbook of Wound Surgery), Strasbourg, 1517. The inscription: "You should elevate the skull

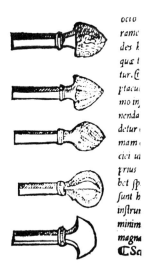

octo
rame
des l
qua t
tur.(t
placu
mo in
nenda
detur
mam
cici ut
prius
bet sp.
funt h
inftrun
minim
magna
℃ Sa

Figure 16. Drill points from Berengario da Carpi's "Tractatus Perutilis et Completus de Fractura Cranei," Venice, 1535.

ment from sinking down into the brain. Here are Scultetus' original words on the subject: "A most ingenious invention was that of the 'wings' attached to the modiolus that prevents its plunge into the brain substance. Nobody, but my preceptor, Fabricius could fashion such a device although others have tried it. It puts all other instruments whose virtue in perforating the skull was extolled in the past, to shame. It is used by up-to-date surgeons, particularly those of Padua, successors of Fabricius in the profession and practice of surgery, the foremost among them that famous physician, anatomist, surgeon and professor of Padua, Petrus de Marchettis, Knight of St. Mark of Venice, my old time 'condiscipulus' under Hieronymus Fabricius for many years, whose rare operative skill is unparalleled in Italy. . . ."

---

with this instrument when it is bashed in and a piece of it is lodged under the other. . . . The flaps (legs of the instrument) should be placed in the same way (symmetrically) so that they can be positioned anywhere (on the skull) . . . the small screw that you screw or drill into the skull bone should be sharp as you can see from this drawing."

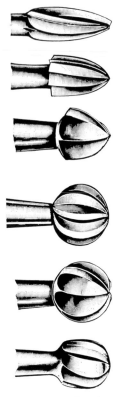

Figure 17. Drills from a current neurosurgical instrument catalogue (V. Mueller, Chicago, 1965).

Here, then, we have the first example of that seemingly modern gadget, the self-arresting drill.

The drill was used by early Greek surgeons to make circles of holes around that part of the skull which had to be removed. Ambroise Paré employed the brace or drill-stock with a binding screw to fix the saw, the drum of which was straight or smooth. Earlier, Berengario da Carpi in his book on head injuries presented crude but adequate illustrations of various drill points, not far remote from the ones in use now (Fig. 16 and Fig. 17).

Somewhat more bizarre was the ferrule, although Scultetus described it as being "very versatile." It was of his own design ("ferrula mea") (Fig. 18). In essence, it was a saw attached to

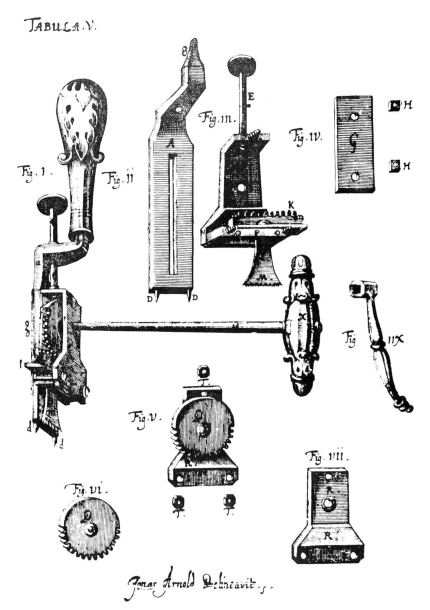

Figure 18. The ferrula of Scultetus and its components.

a cogwheel mechanism. One hand of the surgeon pressed the instrument firmly to the skull in a direction suitable for making a longitudinal groove in the bone. It could not slip because it was firmly anchored to the bone by twin pins. Through a lateral side arm, that jutted out at 90 degrees, a cogwheel was turned around and moved a saw across the line and cut into the skull.

Although Scultetus recommended various forceps and rongeurs for the removal of bone fragments, hammer and chisel were also used. "More prudent and experienced surgeons use forceps for the removal of protruding bones, instead of chisel and mallet, with better results." However, if hammer is being used, it should be made of lead to "avoid reverberating noises ('crepitus') and cerebral concussion."

Silver spatulas, shaped very much like our brain retractors and associated with Harvey Cushing, were used to depress the dura to facilitate the exploration of the epidural space and the removal of purulent material from between the skull and the dura. They were malleable, "fit very nicely between the skull and the membranes," and made of silver instead of iron "because those made of iron might injure the cerebral membranes because of the natural rigidity of the metal."

Chapter 7

THE SURGICAL TREATMENT OF
HEAD INJURIES

⟡⟡

SCULTETUS described the treatment of head injuries according to various categories.

A simple wound of the scalp down to the pericranium should be treated by simple dressing alone. In a similar fashion, no surgical procedure is indicated in head injuries with loss of skin over the skull.

On the other hand, *injuries involving the pericranium* are considered more serious because "if the wound edges do not stick together the pericranium is apt to form a gap and could become inflamed and infection of the bone and subsequent inflammation of the dura mater could easily develop." The surgical treatment should start with the removal of hair around the wound edges and the application of hemp mixed with egg white over the edges of the wound to stop the bleeding. Then, cooling and astringent oils should be applied over the pericranium to prevent inflammation. All this should be kept in place by a dressing made of waxed linen strips. The dressing should be frequently changed—"the outpouring from the wound of exudative fluids is removed," because it soaks into the hemp and linen. It is important to observe at every change of dressing whether "the wound generates good pus or not, that is to say, pus that is white and smells not badly." The dressing should be changed daily until new growth of flesh is noticed. "The linen tapes should be soaked in both red and white wine since these have astringent qualities. On the other hand, rose oil should be avoided, although this is widely used in these wounds by barbers."

Comment. Scultetus preferred his wounds to be packed or widely drained and heal by granulation rather than being sewn up. One wonders what he did in large scalp avulsions. He must have sewn them up or at least approximated the gaping wound edges since needles and thread were part of his armamentarium. Earlier, Ambroise Paré had already described this technique: "... I returned this scalp flap in its proper place and made several stitches, left a little separated to prevent pain and inflammation building up, which happens often when drainage starts. To hold together the parts that were distant and separated, and to prevent entrance of air, which does much harm to such wound, I put long flat tents into the lower edges of the wound so the matter could drain out."[16(p32)]

The treatment of head wounds by Scultetus did not differ much from methods used as early as the tenth century. Linen, silk, or hemp was stuffed into the wound, and the dressing was soaked in egg white, sometimes mixed with rose water and other ingredients. This was changed twice daily in winter and three times in summer.[27] Theodoric[28] applied compresses soaked in wine to the wound. The tannin content of the crude wines of these ages, particularly of the red wines that were preferred for dressings, supplied the desired "astringent qualities." In the late 1300's, John of Mirfield[25] used compresses wrung out in rose oil mixed with egg white "to fill in the wound in the skin which is over the cranium." Marine sponge, carefully washed and dried, had been customarily employed to take up the putrid products from the outside, just like a blotter.

The famous digestive ointment of Ambroise Paré was quite similar; it consisted of egg yolk, oil of roses, and turpentine. He used it first as an emergency measure in 1536 when he ran out of oil; cauterization of gun shot wounds, believed to be poisonous, with boiling oil having been the common way of treatment. The result astounded Paré, then a young and inexperienced military surgeon: "Those on whom I have used the digestive medication feeling little pain in their wounds, without inflammation and swelling, having rested well through the night. The others on whom I had used the oil I found feverish, with great pain, swelling and inflammation around their wound."[16(p57)] The application of the digestive ointment to gunshot wounds was undoubtedly a major discovery, but as far as the treatment of head injuries is concerned, it was old practice. One wonders whether Paré's knowledge of this might not have guided him to apply it to bullet wounds.

Superficial injuries to the skull should be treated by simple dressing. However, Scultetus quotes Berengario da Carpi, who recommended that the skull be abraded if there is any darkening or discoloration of the superficial layer of the bone. Scultetus agrees with this view and suggests that in such instances the surface of the exposed skull be abraded with a raspatorium. The reason for this measure is logical. Scultetus points out that timid surgeons ("timidiores chirurgi") fail to take appropriate steps even when the bone is darkened or changed in appearance and "let nature take its course by sloughing off the involved portion of the bone which is not the right way of treatment since it protracts and delays recovery."

The following was the treatment for a *capillary (hairline), nonpenetrating skull fracture:* "A prudent surgeon who treats head injuries which leave the bone of the skull denuded, clears the surface of the wound by the application of rose oil and abrasion of soft tissues and then diligently explores the surface of the bone both with instruments and by using his eyes to detect any fracture that has to be suspected in these kind of injuries. The proper surgeon, unlike vulgar barber surgeons, enlarges the wound with his knife either in cruciate or triangular fashion, dilates the wound and after removing the pericranium with his fingernails over the suspected area surveys the fracture and damage." If there is no reason for perforation, the wound is treated by packing and dressing.

However, when a fracture is suspected to penetrate through the entire thickness of the bone, trephination over the fracture line might be in order. The fracture is exposed; the wound edges are covered with a concentric row of narrow strips of linen or silk, and a trephine is centered on the fissure in the bone. After pure pus ("pus laudabile") appears from the hole, digestive salves are applied. Eventually the wound becomes filled with granulation tissue; this should be cauterized from time to time to promote healing. Scultetus mentions a number of patients by

name whom he cured in this fashion, including one whose fracture crossed the coronal suture.

Comment. This prophylactic trepanation, certainly unwar-
ranted in the majority of cases by modern standards, was a legacy from Hippocratic times and survived well into the seventeenth century. Scultetus mentioned his trepanation over the coronal suture with some pride. Since antiquity, this location was
avoided by surgeons, if possible, although Berengario da Carpi
mentioned a century before that cranial sutures could be perforated with impunity. Still, catastrophic bleeding from the
sagittal or transverse sinus must have accompanied careless trepanation over the sagittal or lambdoid suture, serving warning
for generations of surgeons. More poetic was the reason of
Arab surgeons to avoid the sutures. They believed that the cranial sutures represented the patient's destiny, written by the
hand of Allah—and who would dare to tamper with that!

In *linear fractures penetrating through both tables,* Scultetus
opposes "the custom of some surgeons who pry these fracture
open," because the use of the handle of the scalpel or dissector
could easily injure the cerebral membranes. Furthermore, he believes that the small amount of "noxious material" that accumu-
lates inside or under the fracture frequently escapes to the surface without any surgical manipulation. However, when a fracture of the internal table is accompanied by the formation of
copious material between skull and dura mater, the surgeon
should not hesitate to use his trephine.

Comment. Ambroise Paré did not hesitate to use the trepan
when he suspected pus beneath the bone. He sometimes depressed the dura, as did Scultetus, to facilitate the egress of
blood or pus. Paré also applied an ingenious method to get the
"noxious material" out by increasing the intracranial pressure:
"I put in a lead pipe or cannula . . . to extract the discharge
which gathered between the dura and the bone. When dressing
him, I had him keep his head low, close his mouth and nose, and
blow to expel the discharge. Then I washed out the wound with
a little syringe. . . ."[16(p36)]

Apart from secondary infection through dirty wounds and

osteomyelitis, the "accumulation of blood" between the internal table and dura or brain, in other words, epidural or subdural hematoma, was very much on the minds of the surgeons of the sixteenth and seventeenth centuries. It was first described articulately by Berengario da Carpi in his book on head injuries in 1518. Ambroise Paré was not only familiar with the countre-coup type of brain injury,[16(p24-25)] but also described a bona-fide subdural hematoma in no lesser person but King Henri II of France, who died eleven days after he was struck in the head by a lance in a tournament which caused "much commotion and shaking of the brain. . . ." "After his death, a quantity of blood was found collected between the dura and the pia mater in the area opposite the blow."[16(p26-27)]

In *skull fractures with fragments penetrating inside the cranium,* Scultetus advises thorough exploration and removal of the fragments down to the dura mater. He advocates trephination in order to evacuate material that might have collected around the fragments, unable to escape through the fracture line (Fig. 19). This is not necessary when the fracture line is large, and the pus is able to escape through it. In these cases, a strip of linen dipped in rose oil should be placed in the gaping fracture. Scultetus used this method successfully on several occa-

Figure 19. Probing under fracture line through a triangular flap (VII) with the lenticulus (IIX) and removal of a fragment with forceps (IX).

sions, including the case of Joannes Anwander, a hunter from the village of Kürchdorf, whose fracture was so wide "I was able to insert my index finger in the fracture with the greatest of ease." "Unfortunately, trephination is carried out frequently even in these cases because of either the ignorance or the avarice of the physician."

Comment. Scultetus and others advocated the removal of bone fragments and chips. What they did with the resulting skull defect depended on its size and on the individual decision of the surgeon. Ambroise Paré was worried about leaving large cranial defects unattended. Once, after having successfully debrided a rather large compound skull fracture, he "recalled . . . that Hippocrates and other good practitioners had always advised against leaving the brain uncovered if possible. I wiped away the blood covering the dura mater, which I could see pulsating strongly, turned the piece of separated bone and replaced it. To hold it better, I sutured the overlying parts in three places. . . ."[16(p23)] Cranioplasty as a separate, secondary procedure was, of course, out of the question. Still, something had to be done and in another patient "after healing of his wound, the scar remained depressed, as Hippocrates wrote, and because of this, to prevent external injuries, I had made for this lackey a helmet of molded leather which he wore until the scar was very solid and the area reinforced."[16(p32)]

Fractures with lesions of the dura mater were treated in a similar fashion with strips of Chinese silk dipped in rose oil inserted between the bone edges, down to the dura. Upon the appearance of laudable pus, honey was added to the rose oil "to cleanse the membranes." If access to the dura was impossible because of overlapping bone edges, the skull was perforated.

Comment. Linen and silk were used for drainage, and care was taken that this drainage system worked. The dura was considered as an important barrier from antiquity on, and Berengario da Carpi thought that its injury or incision during surgery was extremely dangerous, undoubtedly because of the frequency of fatal infections.

Head injuries with lesion of the pia mater and brain sub-

stance were considered very serious. "In wounds which penetrate the pia mater and perhaps the brain substance itself, one has to abstain from all medication that contains oil or fats because the brain substance easily undergoes putrefaction." "Even rose oil has to be avoided because of its heat-generating and acrimonious properties." Honey and rose syrup should be used instead.

Comment. The dura was never incised deliberately, and as far as the brain tissue is concerned, it was definitely "off limits" for the surgeon. Although Guy de Chauliac was said to know that loss of brain tissue is not necessarily fatal, the rumor that he removed part of the brain successfully rests on somewhat shaky grounds. While deliberate tampering with the brain was to be avoided at all cost, loss of brain substance in severe injuries followed by survival was known to occur. Paré described several cases where the patient recovered in spite of lacerating injury to the brain. One of them was a page who suffered a wound "in the right parietal area, with fracture and separation of the bone so that brain substance, the size of half of a filbert, escaped. Seeing this, I pronounced the wound a deadly one. At this, a young physician came up and argued vigorously against me, saying this was not brain substance but a piece of fat. I told him to keep the stuff while I dressed the patient and I would prove what I said to be true. After treating the page, to prove by reason and experience that this piece of brain could not be fat, I told him that what is inside the skull cannot be fat although the parts be cold, because of the great quantity of very hot and subtle animal spirits and the heat of the vapors from all parts of the body rising to the head, such things prevent the development of fat. As for experience, in the dissection of dead bodies, fat had never been found there. Yet, he wished to gain his end by continuing to protest. Finally, I told him that experiments would give us the answers. Several gentlemen and others present wanted to see this. So, I held that if this was fat, it should float in water; contrarily, if it was brain substance it would sink. Moreover, if it was fat, it should melt in a hot pan; if it was brain, without frying or liquifying, it should desiccate and become dry as parchment and finally burn, because it is sticky, humid and watery. These things were done and proved my assertions. Yet, even though the page had lost a part of his brain, he recovered, although he remained deaf thereafter."[16(p39)]

Contusion of the head without laceration of the skin and resulting in swelling of the scalp, eyelids, and sometimes face can be "miraculously cured by the local application of the hide of recently killed animals, particularly dogs or mice. These applications, by creating local heat, inhibit the contusion and result in about twenty hours in a decrease of the swelling. If the contusion does not resolve after the application of the first skin, it should be removed and others put on. Since it is occasionally difficult to get hold of dog or mouse skin, I personally prefer the skin of lamb which can be easily obtained at any hour and has the same properties. With this method, I have treated many children and adults in Ulm."

Among his observations, Scultetus described such treatment, one in a patient with severe contusion and seizures (Obs. XVI), the other in a patient with depressed skull fracture who refused trephination (Obs. XX).

Depressed skull fracture in children, under intact skin, is next described. "The edge of the fracture is simple and the center is depressed. It frequently occurs in children under unbroken skin and without any obvious division of the bone, except for the depression. It has been described by Ambroise Paré. The most ingenious Fabricius Hildanus also recognized this condition and suggested the elevation of the depressed bone with his terebra, devised for this purpose. In my opinion, this operation in small children is not necessary. On the other hand, such depression in older children is incurable because it results in the compression of the brain together with its ventricles and, therefore, the ventricles are not able to elaborate the animal spirit which is necessary to distribute motor power and sense to the whole body. . . ." Scultetus warns against surgery in these cases. His warning is based on technical grounds: "When the instrument [called *torcular* and consisting of a tripod with a central screw to insert into and elevate the depression] is applied to the center of the depression, the central depression can actually be increased," and ". . . when the torcular is inserted in the skull down to the diploe, it is easy to perforate the internal table and injure the dura mater. . . . For any or all of these reasons, it is therefore wiser to omit surgical procedures in this affliction. I, therefore, advise surgeons to abstain from this operation and apply lamb skin to the local contusion. . . ."

Comment. Scultetus was well acquainted with the "ping-pong" fracture of infants and probably well aware of the fact that they occasionally disappear either spontaneously or upon molding of the head. However, the grave prognosis in depressed fractures of older children is hard to understand; it must have been based upon bad experience in patients who also suffered severe cerebral contusion. The rationalization in form of decreased production of "spiritus animalis" illustrates that while the practical treatment of head injuries developed along modern lines in the 1630's, the concept of brain function remained steeped in antiquity. Ever since the fifteenth century, depressions of the skull were elevated by tripods. They utilized central screws and must have been both dangerous and ineffective as Scultetus realized.

Simple depression with intact skin in adults "never occurs without fracture." This condition is rare, but when it occurs, it should be treated surgically even when no fracture is visible in

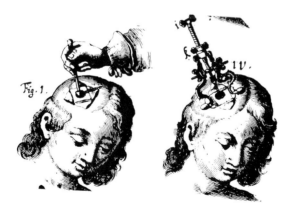

Figure 20. Exploration of depression with probe (I) and application of the three-legged elevator (IV).

the external table, because it might be restricted to the internal table which then "together with blood, descends upon the cerebral membranes without any chance for the blood to escape." Elevation should be performed by using the three-legged terebra "in such a fashion that the center pin perforates the center of the depression not only in the external table but deeper." (See Fig. 20.)

Essentially the same treatment is advocated in *depressions associated with various injuries to the scalp and fractures,* with the exception that a different surgical technique is applied in the presence of wide fracture lines. Here a trephination is advised, not necessarily in the center, "with the application thereafter of the ferrula with which some of the fragments can be elevated, others are removed with instruments similar to tooth extractors." (See Fig. 21.)

Comment. In these cases, Scultetus used modern techniques. The instrument used for elevation resembled a sturdy curved dissector. The tooth extractors for the removal of wedged-in fragments could pass as single-action rongeurs these days.

Although superficial wounds of the temporal muscle are dismissed lightly, Scultetus considers *wounds of the temporal muscle with injury to the blood vessels and pericranium* extremely

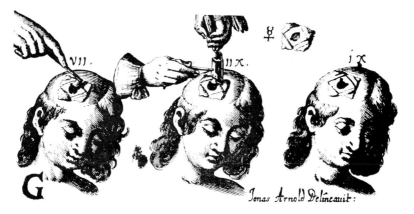

Figure 21. Repair of depressed skull fracture (inset) with saw (VII), ferrula (IIX), and the end result (IX).

dangerous, because "the pericranium is immediately adjacent to the muscle, but, on the other hand, it extends into the interior of the skull through the suture." "Therefore, an inflammation [of the pericranium] is conducted to the dura and from there possibly to the pia mater and then it might involve the substance of the brain itself." Severe bleeding from torn temporal vessels occurs frequently; fortunately this arterial bleeding can be brought to a halt by the application of plaster of Galen, consisting of aloe, rabbit hair, egg white, etc. If the bleeding is so severe that it cannot be stopped by locally applied dressing, one "should also apply a plaster around the neck, composed of a mixture of clay, herbs and essence of roses. This plaster must be four fingers wide and placed transversely around the neck and allowed to dry."

Comment. It is interesting that Scultetus did not mention the technique of hemostasis by ligature. The ligature of bleeding arteries of the scalp was already strongly advocated by Paré to avoid great blood loss. Paré also described a method of transfixing the scalp layers with a suture to control such a bleeding artery.[16(p22)] His case reports describe ligature of the temporal artery[16(p160)] and external jugular vein[16(p161)] in wounds of the head and neck with severe bleeding. The ligature of major blood vessels was one of Paré's most revolutionary inventions; until his time, bleeding was stopped only by applying cautery to the wound. However, none of the surgeons in the sixteenth through the seventeenth centuries attempted ligation of the carotid artery. This was not done until the late eighteenth century, possibly by Abernethy in 1798 for the first time.

Injuries of the temporal muscle associated with compound skull fracture need surgical attention, but interestingly enough Scultetus warns strongly against cutting the fibers of the temporal muscle transversely during the dilatation of the wound because "this can lead to unpredictable trouble." He is in favor of packing the wound. Whether the bone fragments press upon the dura or even lacerate it, "in neither case should the wound be dilated with the scalpel, nor should the edge of the fracture be abraded, nor should the skull be perforated."

Comment. This represents a striking deviation from his usually aggressive approach to similar situations. One must attribute it not so much to a fear of injuring the temporal artery (since he knew how to control this), but perhaps to a knowledge of and healthy respect for the trouble arising from injury to the middle meningeal artery. He followed Ambroise Paré here, who in a similar case (fracture of the petrous bone with contusion of the temporal muscle without laceration) was advised "opening the muscle to apply the trepan to extract the broken bone. I opposed this course on the authority of Hippocrates. In writing on head injuries, he forbade making an incision in such a place, to avoid the accident mentioned earlier. Also by our

Figure 22. Cauterization of the bregma.

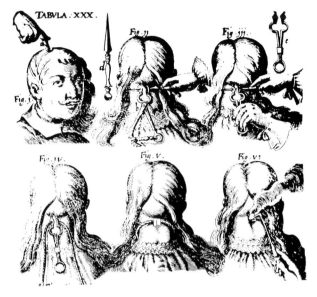

Figure 23. Immobilization of patient's head through nuchal traction.

own experience, those whose muscle has been cut fall in convulsions and die. But the opening can be made above the muscle, as near the fracture as possible without touching the muscle any more than necessary. . . . And thus accord was reached that the incision would be made above the muscle, which I did at once," and from there, somewhat remotely the bone fragments were removed.[16(p35)]

An interesting procedure, described by Scultetus and obviously not related to the treatment of head injuries, is the cauterization of the fontanelles in infants or children or, more frequently, the cauterization of the juncture of certain sutures in adults. The indication of this operation remains somewhat obscure, although he mentioned that it was performed "with good result to prevent or cure epilepsy, apoplexy and vertigo." Although he pointed out in the text that this was also done in infants and children, hydrocephalus was not specifically mentioned. However, this should be kept in mind because already at the end of the thirteenth century Gulielmus da Saliceto described the treatment of hydrocephalic children by removing the fluid through a small hole made in the head by cautery.[29] It is most likely that the operation presented by Scultetus corresponds to the so-called sincipital mutilation.[30] This was already practiced in Neolithic times and consisted of cauterizations of the skin affecting the pericranium along the sagittal suture and the two parietal eminences. Similar cauterizations were done in medieval Europe in cases of epilepsy and dementia.

Scultetus cauterized the junction of the coronal and sagittal sutures (Fig. 22). He used an iron instrument, originally invented by Fabricius ab Aquapendente and called *cannula*. The skin over the area to be cauterized was firmly pressed down with an iron ring attached to a long-handled instrument. Within this ring was applied the heated, solid end of another device that fitted into the ring snugly. This tool also had a long handle made of wood or bone, so when the end was heated red hot, it would not burn the surgeon's hand. As far as the patient was concerned, the procedure was obviously not painless, because at this point Scultetus found it appropriate to describe the ingenious method of Fabricius Hildanus to keep the patient immobilized, particularly "when one does not have an assistant or helper." Actually, the patient's head was held steady by grabbing the scruff of his neck with a large forceps, each blade of which was perforated. A needle and waxed thread was then passed through the intervening soft tissues and spinous processes or interspinous ligaments (Fig. 23). Although Hildanus used this method to realign the cervical spine after fracture,[31] it seems to have been used by Scultetus mostly as a holding maneuver.

Chapter 8

THE TECHNIQUE OF CRANIOTOMY

◇◇◇

*O*NE can reconstruct a typical craniotomy in vivid detail from various chapters of the *Armamentarium Chirurgicum*. It seems that trephination was never performed as an emergency measure, but only after the patient had been observed for some time. However, in compound comminuted skull fractures "on the second or third day after the injury when the patient's strength returns and his condition becomes stabilized, the surgeon should perforate the skull with the modiolus. After the third day the use of the modiolus is dangerous." This implies that after three days there is danger in injuring the dura during trephination which makes one wonder whether the surgeons of that age already had some knowledge of posttraumatic brain swelling that reaches its height at twenty-four to thirty-six hours after the head injury. This assumption might be supported by the following statement: "It is therefore important to perform this operation at a relatively early time, unless, of course, the surgeon is inclined to believe in astrology which prescribes that trephination is dangerous at the time of the full moon because then the brain is swollen and closely adjacent to the inside of the skull and, therefore, the dura is easily injured by the trephine." This ironic passage leaves little doubt in one's mind that Scultetus did not believe in astrological superstitions. Nevertheless, the view that constellations, and particularly the moon, can cause swelling of the brain was still prevalent in the early seventeenth century. It can be traced back to Guy de Chauliac who warned surgeons against trephination at the time of the full moon.

Once the decision was made to go ahead the patient was positioned and the instruments laid out on trays (Fig. 24). The skin was incised in a cruciate manner or by turning down a small, triangular flap (Fig. 25). The latter was preferred when the ex-

Figure 24. Craniotomy set included knife, forceps, lenticulus, trephines of various sizes (with and without center pins), probes, dissector, linen strips, sponges, needle and thread, rose oil, and dressing.

posure was made over structures considered particularly dangerous, such as the temporal muscle or the cranial sutures. In the temporal region, the incision was curved to avoid a transverse cut through the muscle fibers. The wound edges were then spread apart and protected by the application of narrow strips of linen (Fig. 25), very much like our cottonoid patties. Bleeding from the soft tissues was controlled by pouring red wine over the wound edges.

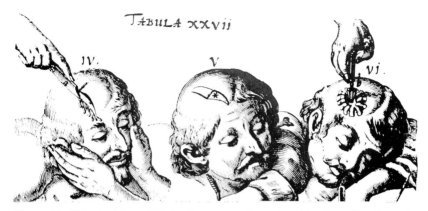

Figure 25. Skin incision (IV) leading to a triangular skin flap (V). X marks the spot for the burr hole which is done after the area is carefully isolated by a concentric row of linen strips (VI).

Next came the removal of the pericranium. This was done according to the method first described by Ambroise Paré. The pericranium, which is very sensitive (maxime sensibiles), can be stripped from the bone by a forceps, the handle of a knife, or by the thumb and index finger of the surgeon. Fingers are best: "Experience showed that they are better than any instrument provided that the fingernails are long enough." Now a trephine, usually the modiolus, is applied to the skull. A small depression is made in the bone to accommodate the center pin and to keep the trephine firmly engaged. The modiolus must be held firmly so it does not wobble during the perforation. Prior to its application, the instrument is dipped in cold water or rose oil, otherwise the drilling "creates heat in the bone and this, in turn, inflames the cerebral membranes." The modiolus is rotated rapidly, but "one must be careful when the trephine approaches the internal table to prevent it from plunging into the brain substance. The proximity of the brain can usually be felt because under pressure with the instrument the internal table (tabula interna or vitrea) moves slightly." Several holes can be drilled if necessary; they can be connected with rongeurs. There were many alternate ways to perform the craniotomy (Figs. 26 and 27).

The wound was left open and packed with flax or hemp,

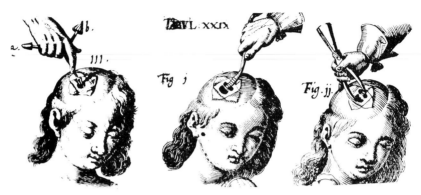

Figure 26. Burr hole is made by the terebra triformis (III) and enlarged by connecting the holes with an elevator (I) or with the instrument of Ambroise Paré (II).

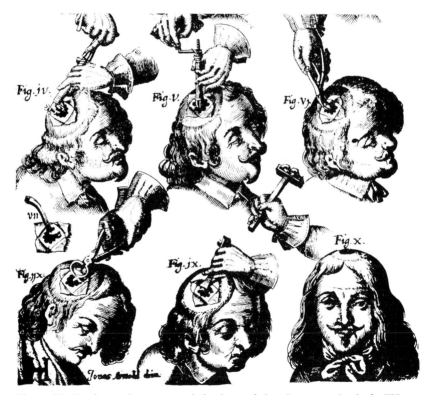

Figure 27. Further enlargement of the bony defect by parrot-beaked (IV) or vulture-beaked (V) instruments, rongeurs (VI, IIX), or by using hammer and chisel (IX). The underlying dura is protected by a silver spatula (VII).

dipped in a mixture of egg white and rose oil. It was thought that this not only protects the cerebral membranes, but also converts the wound exudate into good, laudable pus, the fond wish of all surgeons until the Listerian era. Scultetus considered adequate drainage by strips of linen or Chinese silk down to the depth of the wound extremely important, "to let the pus drain out . . . so that it could not extend or propagate along the membranes of the brain." Upon the appearance of the "pus laudabile," the packing of the wound must be discontinued. From then on it was simply covered by a dressing, sometimes soaked in astringent oils. This was followed by dressings of linen soaked in wine, until scarring of the wound occurred. Although sutures were applied in other wounds, they were not used in injuries of the head, and healing by primary intention was not considered important. The head dressing was ingenious. Scultetus was not the inventor of the "Scultetus binder" for nothing! He applied a somewhat modified form of this binder to the head (Fig. 28). This consisted of a square or oblong piece of cloth, the opposite sides having been fashioned into four flaps. These flaps were lettered in the illustration for easy identification. By tying different combinations of opposite flaps together, well-fitting head dressings could be produced conforming to the area of the head to be covered. These snug dressings not only followed the contour of the head, but also left two of the opposite flaps free to be tied under the chin for keeping the bandage firmly in place in restless patients.

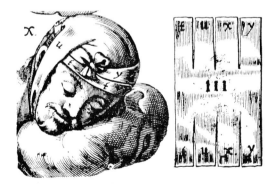

Figure 28. Head dressing with binder devised by Scultetus.

The standard technique of Scultetus was hardly different from the trephination described by John of Mirfield in his *Breviarium Bartholomei* (1380-1396): ". . . having removed the bone in part or altogether as far as the dura mater, you may take clear pieces of linen, pour rose oil on two of them and rose honey on one, and place them between the cranial bone and the dura mater, obliquely and gently; and you should place piece upon piece, gently until the opening in the skull is filled with these pieces. And afterwards, with compresses wrung out in rose oil mixed with egg white warm, fill in the wound in the skin which is over the cranium, etc. . . ."[25] He also warned: "When it is necessary to work on the skull with instruments, fill the ears of the patient with cotton so he may not hear the cracking sound of iron on bone."[25]

Compare this with the craniotomy described by John Atkins in "The Navy Surgeon," published in 1734: The operation should be performed in the hold of the ship, "in a close place, by candlelight" since air is "an enemy to the brain." Round and round turns the drill "dipped in rose oil" while the patient's ears are plugged with wool "for preventing an ungrateful sensation." From time to time bone dust is wiped away with a feather brush. The surgical technique remained essentially the same over the span of 350 years.

It is a popular idea that operations in centuries bygone were carried out in patients made insensitive by liquor, since they were done without any kind of anesthesia. Far from it! Temperance was stressed by Scultetus. One can sympathize with these patients, many of them grizzled veterans of the war, whose wounds were copiously irrigated with wine, but who were not allowed to take a good swig of it. Scultetus with his student years in Padua and his experience as a military surgeon could not possibly have been a prude, yet his words sound pedantic: "These wounds [those of the head] can sometimes heal without trephination in a man of sound character and good health. . . . However, it is important to prescribe good living habits for patients with head injuries, the most important being a complete abstinence from Bacchus and Venus." He elaborated on this in one of his Observations (XIV) with the appropriate title: "A case of head injury with opening of the skull that became lethal because the patient drank forbidden wine." He described the case of a young cloth dryer who was hit on the head by drunken travelers. Free fragments of the compound fracture were removed, but the patient continued to have "considerable inflammation of the wound" and severe headaches. Scultetus immediately suspected "an accumulation of purulent material under the skull impinging upon the cerebral membranes." "I was of the opinion that the wound should be opened with the modiolus and the material which accumulated under the skull should be removed together with the bone fragments responsible for it." He trephined and found the dura inflamed; this did not satisfy him, and he drilled again to find the suspected pocket of pus. This he did on the second attempt, on the tenth day: "After the second perforation with the modiolus I saw a piece of bone split off the internal table, perforating the cerebral membranes. I was able to remove this fragment." "Shortly afterward, the patient drank a large amount of wine, although this was forbidden to him. This resulted in the formation of an inflammation of the cerebral substance causing fever, delirium, and convulsions spreading over the whole body and this eventually led to death." The wine apart, what a good description of acute meningoencephalitis!

Chapter 9

MEDICAL MANAGEMENT

◇◇◇

SUPPORTING treatment consisted of drugs, blood-letting, and innumerable enemas that conjure the life of Moliére's "Malade Imaginaire." Wine, as we have seen, was strictly forbidden in head injuries; cold julip and barley water were recommended for fever. The use of laudanum or opium for pain was frequent; this was well established since antiquity and strongly recommended by Guy de Chauliac.

The wonder drug of the era, concocted by physicians and laymen alike, the truly universal panacea, was the theriac. Its composition varied. It was frequently held secret. It was given internally and externally, on wounds, in the boiling oil used for bullet wounds, and on stumps of amputated limbs, on snake bites, etc. Ambroise Paré, a man of eminent common sense, was rather contemptuous of many esoteric remedies of his age. His "digestive dressing" made of egg yolk, oil of roses, and turpentine was certainly simpler and more benign than many others in vogue, such as the concoction shown to him by an Italian surgeon that was made by boiling newly whelped puppies in oil of lilies and mixing it with earthworms prepared in turpentine of Venice! Neither did Paré believe in the curative power of mummies, dried pieces of usually fake Egyptian mummies given to the patient. But he did use theriac and obviously believed in it since he recorded several formulas for its preparation. The common denominator, and obviously the *pièce de résistance* of all types of theriac, was the flesh or venom of vipers, and Paré himself was once bitten on the finger by handling a viper in an apothecary shop.[9]

Theriac was as popular as ever in the seventeenth century, the forerunner of all patent snake-oil medicines to come. It was sold on the market place, an easy and well-established way to fleece the gullible public (Fig. 29). The eighth chapter of *Sim-*

Figure 29. Theriac vendor at a fair. Print from the 1683 edition of *Simplicissimus*.

plicissimus is entirely devoted to it and appropriately entitled: "How to Become a Traveling Swindler." The hero bought all the necessary ingredients to concoct his "Theriaca Diatessaron." He seemed to have skipped the snakes, probably difficult to obtain, and selected herbs, roots, butters, and oils "potent enough to cure all ailments, even those of a horse." As proof of its power, he placed a frog into the jar in front of the gaping peasants. The unfortunate and originally lethargic frog hopped madly in the brew and proved the point. To overcome any remaining sales resistance, he found it "very important to put the salve in little boxes made of tin or paper or in glass phiols," and "to make it more presentable I let a flyleaf printed in French to explain to all and sundry how and what it is good for."

Popular as theriac might have been, Scultetus, a learned and conscientious physician, had nothing to do with it. Although an occasional item of interest crops up among his formulas, such as Sanguis draconis, or dragon blood, for eye troubles, most of his prescriptions are made of identifiable and relatively simple vegetable and mineral components. These include poppy, violet, ginger, oil of roses, cinnamon, honey, iris, chamomil, veronica, rhubarb, arnica root, sweet milk of almond, barley flour, domestic bread, powdered red coral, boric acid, salt, alum, turpentine, magnesium tartar, and Peruvian balsam. It is obvious that the mysterious theriac was by this time relegated by educated physicians to the charlatans and mountebacks of the fairs. Compare this with the recipes of another surgeon of renown, Matthäus Gottfried Purmann, who recommended in his "Chirurgia Curiosa" salves made of earthworms, human mummy, hog brain, and "the moss of a man's skull that was either killed or hung, and gathered when the star of Venus predominates!"

Blood-letting was another matter! As for any other ailment, in head injuries blood was made to flow freely. Indeed, repeated and massive blood-letting was customary to reduce fever and "phlegmonous inflammation of the wound." Many of Scultetus' patients were bled daily. It is anybody's guess what the total loss might have been, but rough calculations show that they were exorbitant on occasion. Ambroise Paré presented a case where vigorous bleeding was induced intermittently for three days. The total blood loss, according to Hamby's calculations and measured by Paré in "pallettes," amounted to five pints. The patient "being vigorous and strong" recovered from both injury and treatment. Paré's final sentence in describing this case certainly rings true in more ways than one: "he was entirely cured, thanks to God, without Whose benediction these treatments would have been useless."[16(p30-31)]

Little is being mentioned about hospitals in the surgical texts, and perhaps the less they were mentioned the better. At the time of the Thirty Years' War, most hospitals were still church-supported, although municipal hospitals were also erected under the jurisdiction of city councils. It is apparent from a few remarks of Scultetus that such a municipal hospital existed in Ulm. These hospitals were directed by a physician, appointed by the city administration or by the religious order in charge. He was invariably overworked. If he was young, educated, and humanitarian, patients received at least some medical attention. More often, the physician pocketed his salary and was rarely seen on the premises. Patients helped each other as best they could, and in good weather gathered in the courtyard, the maimed helping the maimed (Fig. 30). Inside, the hospitals were suffocating, the

Figure 30. The hospital. Etching by Jacques Callot.

windows never open, patients, living and dying, stretched out on rotting straw, sometimes three to five to a bed, many on the floor. Nuns, when available, in hospitals managed by religious orders alleviated some of the suffering, but in public or municipal hospitals, nursing was virtually nonexistent or deplorable. Many of the nurses were drunken harridans, and any patient with money was liable to be robbed by them. During the night, there was nobody on whom to call.

Chapter 10

CASE HISTORIES

◇◇

*T*HE second part of Scultetus's book describes one hundred detailed case histories. Thirty-one of the 140 pages of this part of the *Armamentarium,* or twenty-three out of the hundred cases, are devoted to injuries of the skull or brain.

There was obviously no lack of action as far as the small community of Ulm and its environs was concerned during the latter part of the Thirty Years' War. Ulm might have been relatively quiet when it came to major engagements of the war, but life was turbulent just the same.

Of the twenty-three observations on head injuries, seven involved fights in battle or brawls between soldiers, Imperial (usually Austrian of the Holy Roman Empire), Swedish, Bavarian. For example: ". . . an Imperial soldier of Austrian origin" was treated "after his encounter in battle with a Swedish horseman during our sad Teutonic War. This soldier received two blows on the occiput, collapsed, and was captured by his enemies. He was delivered to the hospital of the community of Ulm, half-dead" (Obs. VIII). The usual scenes of war and marauding prevailed: "This incident again occurred during the war when the patient was set upon in his house and was hit over the vertex of his head with the handle of a sword" (Obs. IX). Or there is also the case of poor Maria Lutzen who "in the month of September of 1637 was badly treated" (obviously raped) "by Bavarian soldiers" and suffered contusion of the head (Obs. XXII). In six other cases the victims, peasants, merchants, or craftsmen, were injured by either soldiers or bandits. In some of the case histories, the circumstances of the injury are not described in detail, but only two of them, that of a woman who was hit on the head and a boy who fell, could be classified as truly accidental.

Apart from the war and highway robbery, juvenile delinquency was also well established in Swabia in the early seventeenth

81

century. In Observation XXIII, Scultetus wrote about the story of a farmer who was mercilessly taunted by a group of local boys and girls. Finally, his patience ran out, and he turned on them. The young men grabbed him and lifted him up in the air, upside down, with his feet up and dropped him on his head. This is one of the few occasions in his book when Scultetus lapsed from Latin into German, either from rightful wrath or because he could not translate it correctly. Before dropping him on his head, the youths told him to cut out the foolishness (". . . praesentes juvenculae serio imperarunt, ut tales nugas relinqueret"), "sonst werde ihm der Baum gestellt werden" (Fig. 2). "They left him there, prostrate with blood running from his nose and ears. Some bystanders, having seen him lying on the ground, threw cold water on him which revoked his spirit."

The translation of a typical case history illustrates how detailed they are:

"*Observation I. Head injury with a deep, longitudinal, depressed skull fracture.* In the year 1637, on the 11th day of January, at seven o'clock in the afternoon, Johannes Happelius, Imperial Horse Appraiser, a man of cool and humid temperament and in his 32nd year of age, became involved in a fight with an Imperial Trumpeter (tubicen Caesareus) and received seven wounds. One of these injuries involved the left elbow but the other six were inflicted upon the head. One was behind the left ear, another along the coronal suture, the third near the sagittal suture, the fourth and fifth in the forehead; all of these were rather superficial. However, the sixth of the head injuries was on the right side and quite deep including a cut in the temporal muscle at the level of the coronal suture. This wound penetrated the cranium which was broken and depressed. All of the injuries were cared for by the municipal surgeon of Ulm who treated them in the customary simple fashion. They all healed without trouble except for the wound in the temporal muscle and for this I have been called into consultation. There, a large, depressed skull fracture was visible; this was treated, as is the custom, by dilatation of the wound and application of dressings dipped in egg white and later with plasters concocted of flour of barley and beans, morsels of bread, powder of red roses and red wine. Later, after further dilatation of the wound, a liberal amount of cephalic powder was sprinkled on the dressing applied to the bone. This powder was made of the roots of the Aristolochia plant and of Florentine iris.

"On the 12th of January, following a restless night caused by swelling and pain in the wound, I informed the patient and his relatives that it has become necessary to dilate the wound of the temporal muscle with the knife. I also prescribed a cholagogue syrup to promote the release of bilious material. On the 13th of January, the patient felt somewhat better but on the following day he again complained of severe pain in the wound. After having deliberated the matter with the patient's physician, we again dilated the wound of the temporal muscle with the knife in a triangular fashion and discussed whether a perforation of the skull with the trephine should be attempted in order to elevate the depressed portion of the bone. On the 15th and 16th of January, the painful wound was again reopened several times. Finally, on the 18th, after a very restless night, the wound edges of the temporal muscle were retracted, the periosteum was stripped away with fingernails and the wound was packed with wads of Indian hemp dipped in a soothing powder as well as rose oil and red wine. On the 19th of January, the blood which issued forth after the incision of the skin, pericranium and temporal muscle congealed. This enabled us to have a better survey of the depressed fracture which—as I already indicated—was ready for perforation. On the next day the depressed part of the cranium in the vicinity of the coronal suture was perforated with the trephine and the depression elevated. In the process the dura mater became visible; it was bathed in cold rose oil. The denuded skull was sprinkled with cephalic powder and the wound was covered with a dry dressing. On the following day, the wound looked better and the patient slept through the night. Again, rose oil was poured over the dura and cephalic powder was applied to the skull. From the 22nd to the 26th, the wound showed evidence of healing, but on the 27th, remaining fragments of the depressed fracture including splinters of the internal table were excised with my new instrument."

The following days were spent by repeatedly purging the man

with enemas "to remove bilious and serous humors" from the body of the patient who suffered from severe intestinal cramps and colic. However, the wound was healing, and the dura mater was covered by now with "new red tissue," obviously granulation tissue. Eventually the patient was given a bath, but shortly afterward, on the 11th of February, "he vomited a great amount of bilious material and complained of precordial pain." The vomiting caused a good deal of pain in the head wound, but the precordial pain subsided although the patient was unable to sleep and had to be given Opium Laudanum whereafter he slept quietly for six hours." The wound healed well, but the patient was purged mercilessly over and over again, until the 17th of February, when he "made a public appearance." This was obviously not quite successful because "the cold air induced some colics and pains." They finally subsided, and a few days later the patient became ambulatory and was well on the road to recovery.

Fourteen cases represented fractures or penetrating wounds of the skull of varying severity. Although Scultetus made the startling statement that "depression of the skull in adults rarely develops unless the skull is softer than usual" (Obs. XX), he did not hesitate to trephine and elevate the depressed fragments as soon as possible. However, the operation was frequently delayed since he was usually not called into consultation until several days after injury. In those cases where the dates can be established from the records, radical repair with elevation or removal of the bone fragments was not performed until three, five, six, nine, ten, twelve, and thirteen days later. In some patients, particularly those who were treated initially by barbers, the depressed fracture was not recognized, and repair had to be carried out only after the wound of the scalp healed. It would have perhaps surprised Scultetus would he have known that similar incidents occur in the twentieth century and not only in patients treated by barbers, but by physicians and emergency room interns! His stern admonition still rings true: "The wound should always be inspected and the pericranium removed if necessary to ascertain the presence of fracture [prior to dressing of the wound] because neglect of such a wound might lead to all kinds of trouble and even to death of the patient" (Obs. XXI). He quoted examples when lack of diagnosis or neglect of prompt surgical treatment proved fatal. One of his observations (Obs. IX) is entitled: "Puncture of the cranium with penetration through the dura mater that killed the patient through lack of surgical intervention." This patient suffered depressed skull fracture which resulted in "fever and derangement of the mind. A physician was called who administered laxatives, performed venisection in the arm and prescribed various medications to combat the fever. He left no stone unturned and tried every commonly used instrument to elevate the depression and reduce the bone to its natural configuration but of no avail. However, he did not perform a trephination because he lacked the proper instruments; moreover, he was insecure about his skill in such procedures. As a result, the patient succumbed to the disease. Therefore, it has to be pointed out that in such cases the skull must be perforated with the modiolus in order to elevate the bone fragments that are pressing down on the cerebral membranes; if this would have been done, the patient probably would not have died." This patient, of course, probably died of meningitis and might have done so despite surgical repair, but it is still possible that repair *and* removal of hair and dirt from between and under the fragments might have prevented a fatal course.

The barbers were frequently blamed. There was the case of the patient with a blow to the vertex (Obs. XVIII): "He was treated by a local barber surgeon in a simple way as any other wound would have been treated and was considered cured in seven days. Eight days later, the man started to complain about increased swelling over the injured part of the head as well as headaches. The wound was explored by myself. After dilatation of the wound a fracture of the skull was noticed and a trephination was performed. It was found that the puncture of the skull included both laminae and upon perforation with the modiolus on the 12th day, material that accumulated over the dura mater was removed." A similar situation is described in Observation XIX, where a bath-keeper "treated the wound without realizing that a fissure of the skull was present involving the cerebral membranes and even injury to the cerebral substance itself which developed through the wound. This was a major error." Although the treatment was by now taken over by a physician, "it was fairly long before it was realized what error the balneator has committed by being ignorant about perforation of the skull in general and about the symptoms of this disease in particular." So, now they embarked on the customary course of prolonged treatment with blood-letting and cold enemas.

Scultetus was well aware of the fact that the internal table could be fragmented with chips of bone protruding into the brain substance without any or only minimal changes in the external table, a condition already known to Ambroise Paré.[16(p25)] In one instance (Obs. XIV): ". . . a wound in the occiput partially opened up the lambdoid suture, the rim of this fracture" (which we now would call a diastatic fracture) "forming a depression but only of the internal table. He was treated simply by a barber surgeon. In this particular case purulent material accumulated under the bone which was overlooked because the external table seemed completely intact; the fracture involved only the internal table and therefore remained occult."

Scultetus described his technique of reducing skull fractures in some detail (Obs. VI): "The depression was about one finger deep at the level of the coronal suture but two fingers deep at the level of the sagittal suture. . . . I performed a trephination with the modiolus in the vicinity of the coronal and sagittal sutures. Having perforated the skull and after making various holes in the bone I inserted the lenticulate instrument and reduced the depression. The dura mater was bathed in rose oil and cephalic powder was applied." (See Fig. 19.) Soon afterwards the patient felt better, started to talk, and was able to sleep peacefully. However, about two weeks later, he again became restless, unable to sleep, and complained of severe headache; ". . . therefore . . . I inserted a curved instrument between the external and internal tables of the skull and separated a piece of bone which undoubtedly caused the pain and restlessness.

This piece of skull which was separated and sequestered by nature itself was then extracted." The patient recovered.

Some of these operations were quite formidable. In Observation XII, the depression over the cortex was associated with "a lesion to the dura mater and falx which carries branches of the carotid artery and jugular vein." This was overlooked (by the barber, naturally), and the wound healed by primary intention. "However, the patient continued to have terrible pain, he also had rotating convulsions and, finally apoplexy. Although the injury over the vertex was already healed, I was able to feel with the palpating finger the depth of a maximal depression in the middle of the skull. Therefore, I opened up the skin over the vertex with a knife in a cruciate manner, removed the pericranium and perforated the bone with a trephine around the edge of the depression. I applied rose oil to the dura mater as well as cephalic powder and eventually, with great effort elevated the depressed bone. A great deal of purulent material issued forth. A salve and dressing was then applied to the dura mater while *the falx was incised in a transverse fashion to stop the bleeding.*" The description of this maneuver suggests that Scultetus deliberately sacrificed the superior sagittal sinus to stop the bleeding that arose from it being torn by bone fragments. He must have been very lucky, and the depression was probably within the anterior third of the sinus, or the sinus was perhaps already partly thrombosed because this patient recovered.

These cases illustrate that Scultetus was a bold and aggressive surgeon who did not hesitate to perform radical surgery if it could be of benefit to the patient. He stated flatly that "although a perforation of the skull should be done as soon as possible, recovery after trephination performed several days after injury is still possible." His statistics proved the point. Considering the circumstances, it is surprising that only one of the nine patients whom he trephinated died. On the other hand, four out of five patients who were not operated upon and received only superficial treatment in form of dilatation and cleansing of the soft tissue wound succumbed, mostly from intracranial infection.

Infections were, of course, rampant. On several occasions the dura was already "inflamed" at the time of the craniotomy, although this term might have referred to traumatic and hemorrhagic changes as well as to bacterial infections. However, it is easy to understand that the complete lack of aseptic treatment and the subsequent handling that consisted of the irrigation of the exposed dura with rose oil, the application of the astringent "cephalic powder" to the bone edges, and the open packing of the wound resulted in wound sepsis and frequent osteomyelitis. In almost every operated patient and in some of the nonoperated ones, sequesters formed that had to be removed weeks or months later. Sometimes "semiputrid" (obviously necrotic) "parts of the dura mater had to be removed through the incision with a forceps." However, in the majority of patients, pink granulation tissue covered the dura, and the wound eventually healed.

A deadly complication was the formation of brain abscesses. While epidural empyemas were frequently successfully dealt with, intracerebral abscesses were invariably lethal. Three of these patients are described in detail (Obs. VIII, XIV, and XIX). One was a soldier who suffered a closed head injury from which "he quickly recovered and was walking around with no complaints whatever when he suddenly became somnolent and died." This occurred several weeks after the blow. At autopsy "there was considerable inflammation of the membranes and a large cavity in the brain tissue filled with pus and penetrating into the ventricles." A classic case of posttraumatic frontal abscess which remained silent until it ruptured into the ventricular system!

Another man had a compound skull fracture, inadequately treated. "He died among convulsions and it was found that abscess formed under the broken internal table and ruptured into the right cerebral ventricle."

The third case (Obs. XIX) is interesting. Again, the wound in the occiput was not adequately debrided. The fracture line was so wide that "eventually a cerebral fungus became visible with protrusion of the brain between the wound edges. This prolapse of the brain increased in size and, in time, the right side of the patient became paralyzed. This was followed by convulsions of the right arm." Soon afterwards, the man died. An autopsy was performed: "The entire part of the occipital bone from the lambdoid to the petrous suture was prolapsed." The cerebral fungus subsided after death, but "an abscess was noticed in the prolapsed part of the left side of the brain from which a great amount of odoriferous pus escaped." The hemisphere harboring the abscess was enlarged and filled the interhemispheric space (herniation of the supracallosal cistern!). "The abscess was surrounded by a capsule [folliculus] and there was no evidence of inflammation away from the abscess." On sectioning the brain, it was noticed that "the left ventricle was compressed but limpid, clear fluid escaped from the distended right ventricle." "The choroid plexus of the left ventricle was pale but the one in the right ventricle was reddishly discolored." Here we have an excellent description of a chronic encapsulated abscess in the left hemisphere causing increased intracranial pressure with herniation into the interhemispheric fissure of the enlarged hemisphere, as well as formation of a cerebral fungus through the dural defect, contralateral Jacksonian seizures, hemiplegia, and death by transtentorial herniation! Whatever his reasoning and grasp of the function of the central nervous system was in general, Scultetus was a meticulous and astute observer.

Observation XXIII describes a case of basal skull fracture and cerebral contusion. There was no palpable fracture, and even the scalp was not lacerated, but there was bleeding from the nose and both ears. On the third day, the patient's state of consciousness deteriorated, and he developed fever and convulsions for about four days. "It was thought that he must have severe concussion of the brain." Surgery was not performed, and the patient eventually recovered.

The surgical treatment of an epidural or subdural hematoma represents the subject of Observation XIII. The patient, a cavalry captain, suffered a head injury in September of 1629. The wound healed by primary intention, but many weeks later he started to complain of headache, vertigo, a hot feeling in the eyes, and he developed paralysis in his right arm. Scultetus performed a craniotomy on March 13, 1630: ". . . a considerable amount of blood issued forth from underneath the fractured skull after the trephination was completed. The material that was evacuated was situated over the dura mater which it depressed. . . . After its evacuation the symptoms disappeared."

Two consecutive case histories (Obs. X and XI) represent a very unusual attempt to explain human pathology by its similarity to an animal disease. The first of these observations describes the staggers of sheep; the second, a disease with similar symptoms in man. It deals with vertigo. This condition, "called Wirbling in German, is—according to veterinary surgeons—quite common in the best kind of sheep where it converts to whole brain into water and leads inevitably to death. It can be predicted when the sheep starts showing signs of vertigo and circumgyrations, become finally quite weak. The brain substance becomes very thin under the meninges to such an extent that the anterior ventricles shine through it. However, not a drop of water can be obtained from the third and fourth cerebral ventricles. I found the third ventricle completely filled with blood. However, having lifted up the organ of olfaction on the left side of the brain with a scalpel, a large abscess was found, full of limpid water which propagated into the left eye. It made me wonder a great deal why in the presence of such severe infection of the brain, this sheep showed only the symptom of vertigo without any convulsions or paralysis."

Scultetus then proceeded with the case of a woman whose disease he considered to be analogous or similar to that of the sheep. This woman made a good recovery from a contusion of the head. Nevertheless, after a while she developed severe vertigo followed by "apoplexy" and death. At the postmortem examination "in the left side of the brain a tumor of the size of a hen's egg was found that partially compressed the third ventricle."

What Scultetus noticed as a similarity of the two conditions was obviously severe obstructive hydrocephalus resulting in a huge symmetrical distension of both lateral ventricles. The obstruction developed in the third ventricle; from there on caudally, the ventricular system was not enlarged. In the case of the woman, the mass compressing and obstructing the third ventricle probably represented a tumor. As far as the sheep was concerned, it must have been a cyst caused by the parasite and blocking the passage of cerebrospinal fluid through the interventricular foramen. Staggering, manifested by swaying and uncertain gait is caused by Coenurus cerebralis, the larva of Taenia coenurus found in the brain of sheep, goats, and other ruminants. It intrigued men from antiquity as a peculiar disease, and shepherds occasionally attempted to remove the parasite from the brain with their knives. According to some authorities, this practice might have led originally to trepanation in man, although most experts believe that the theory of veterinary origin of trepanation in man is unlikely. It certainly would not account for prehistoric craniotomies performed before the development of animal husbandry.

Chapter 11

FUNCTION OF THE CENTRAL NERVOUS SYSTEM—ITS CONCEPT IN THE SIXTEENTH–SEVENTEENTH CENTURY

◇◇

*W*HAT did the surgeons who dealt with head injuries think of the function of the brain? They were confused and certainly very cautious in expressing their thoughts. Physiological experimentation did not exist in a modern sense; the brain of animals devoid of an immortal soul, or any soul for that matter, could not possibly be taken as similar in function to that of man, although the morphological similarity was duly recognized. The short supply of brains from human autopsy forced many anatomists from antiquity on to rely on animal brains for dissection with the result that some structures, such as the rete mirabile, a network of blood vessels at the base of the brain of ruminants, were uncritically transferred to human anatomy for centuries. The brain was recognized as the seat of intellect, but the site and *modus operandi* of its various functions remained elusive.

Surgeons of distinction were par force good and sometimes outstanding anatomists. Berengario da Carpi was among the foremost anatomists of his time. In 1522, he published in Bologna *Isagogae Breves Perlucidae ac Uberrimae in Anatomiam Humani Corporis,* a very popular textbook of anatomy with some emphasis on the gross appearance of the nervous system. This book superseded and to some extent corrected the *Anathomia* of Mundinus (Mondino da Luzzi), a perennial best-seller since 1318. Ambroise Paré, although self-taught, was keenly interested in anatomy and published a textbook, *Anatomie Universelle due Corps Humain,* in 1561. Fabricius ab Aquapendente, Scultetus's mentor, was a great anatomist, and the basic knowledge of his pupil was sound for his time. They all were familiar with the monumental work of Andreas Vesalius, *De Humani Corporis Fabrica,* ever since its first edition in 1543.

92

What the surgeons had to rely upon was their clinical observation of brain-damaged patients and the findings at autopsy. The surgical interventions did not furnish much information. These operations were superficial; the surgeons did not venture into the interior. Autopsies were performed frequently as a matter of routine, and both Paré and Scultetus were excellent observers. The Renaissance dispensed with religious opposition to the speculation on the anatomical site of the soul and mental function, at least as far as the official churches were concerned. But public morality was easily offended and superstition among all people, including powerful princes and city fathers, was rampant. One had to tread lightly. Religious dogmas, both Catholic and Protestant, remained rigid and could not be touched upon while discussing soul or intellect.

Actually, these learned physicians, surgeons, and anatomists knew almost nothing about the function of the brain. A very few were frank enough to say so. Here is a disarming passage from Nicolas Stensen's "Dissertation on the Anatomy of the Brain," read at M. Thevenot's house in Paris in 1665, and rediscovered by Gibson:[32] "Instead of promising that I shall satisfy your curiosity in what relates to the Anatomy of the Brain, I begin publicly and frankly owning that I know nothing of the matter . . . it would be a great blessing to Mankind if this most delicate Part, and which is liable to so many dangerous Diseases, were as well understood as the generality of Anatomists and Philosophers imagine it to be. . . . It is very certain that it is the principal Organ of the Soul and the Instrument by which it works very wonderful Effects. The Soul which imagines it can penetrate into everything . . . and . . . nothing in the World can set bounds to its Knowledge, is nevertheless utterly at a loss to describe its own Habitation. . . . We need only view a Dissection of the large Mass, the Brain, to have ground to bewail our ignorance. On the very Surface you see varieties which deserve your admiration; but when you would look into its inner Substance you are utterly in the dark, being able to say nothing more than that there are two Substances one greyish the other white, which last is continuous with the Nerves distributed all over the body; that the greyish Substance serves in some places for a Cortex to the White. . . ."

The grey and white matter and the cerebral convolutions were well known in the sixteenth through seventeenth centuries. Willis, one of the foremost anatomists of the nervous system, described it in his *Cerebri Anatome* of 1664 as follows: "If it be asked what the gyri and convolutions contribute to the brain or for what end its whole twisted structure exists, we say that the brain is so constructed for a more abundant reception of the spiritous nourishment and for a more suitable diffusion of the animal spirits for their uses. In regard to the brain's nourishment, which must be subtle and highly elaborated, it ought not be admitted by too wide an approach but rather by minute pores and passages."[33]

The trouble was that ever since the time of the ancient Greek philosophists, the ventricles of the brain were considered "the central seat of the operations of the mind. The clear fluid there was their vehicle." These are the words of Sir Charles Sherrington: "Judging the brain and nerves to be tenanted by subtle and ultra-tenuous spirits, he [Galen] seems to have said to himself, seeing these chambers, 'This is their reservoir.' "[34] Actually, Galen (A.D. 130-201) placed the soul in the brain substance, one of the very few who did so, but considered the ventricles as the site of the "pneuma," the animal spirit. The original idea goes far beyond the time of Galen. It can be traced back to Herophilos (330-250 B.C.), who first described the cerebral ventricles and considered them the receptacle of the soul. They were believed to be filled with air or gas containing the mysterious "pneuma." It might be surprising, but this theory stood the test of time to such an extent that it hardly could be challenged in its entirety in the mid-seventeenth century.

From a metaphysical point of view, the details were well worked out in the pre-Christian era. The "Princeps Anima," or the Reigning Soul, a phrase which occurs repeatedly in sixteenth century translations of Galen,[35] is contained by the ventricles. To be more exact, the powers of the soul can be separated into the faculties of common sense (sensus communis or sensus communis phantastica or imaginativa), meditation (cogitatio or cogitatio rationalis or formativa), and memory (memoria conservativa or servativa). They are located in the lateral ventricles (cellula prima), third ventricle (cellula secunda), and fourth ventricle (cellula tertia), respectively. The common sense of medieval thought, incidentally, had nothing to do with intelligence. It was considered the meeting place of the five senses and, by transference, the empirical knowledge that arises from the senses.[35]

There was remarkably little variation in this metaphysical order of the soul from the Greek anatomists through Avicenna, Razes to Albertus Magnus, Thomas à Aquinas, and Guy de Chauliac, as Sudhoff so admirably pointed out in his treatise on the history of the ventricular system.[36] A concept held valid with hardly any variation from 300 B.C. to A.D. 1500! No wonder that even men of the Renaissance were reluctant to refute it. Here was a dogma three hundred years older than Christianity itself!

Slight embellishments were added as time went on. Mondino described in his anatomy of the early fourteenth century that the mental operations of the spirit were controlled by the movement of the "red worm" (the choroid plexus of the third ventricle), which opened and closed the passage between the ventricles and directed the flow of animal spirit. Interestingly enough, Leonardo da Vinci also mentioned this.

Actually, the ventricles, choroid plexus, etc. were already known to the ancient Greeks. However, as so frequently happens in the history of science, theoretical speculation and practical observation could not be reconciled; in the long run, theory prevailed. It was a long time before rational thought based on facts allowed scientists to believe what they saw.

Was there a spiritual "pneuma" in the ventricles? Most physicians well into medieval times thought that they are filled with an air-like substance. Galen thought that they contain a watery humor. By the time of the Renaissance, it was impossible to deny the presence of fluid in those chambers of the brain, but there were many ways to dodge the issue. Berengario da Carpi stated in 1521 that "watery excrement can be seen in the majority of the heads dissected and always in the ventricles, although more in some bodies than in others." Some authors believed that fluid appeared only after death as a pathological phenomenon. Varolio in 1573 drew attention to the fact that the ventricles are filled with fluid and not with gaseous pneuma.[37]

Even Vesalius (1543) was strangely ambiguous about the function of the ventricles, perhaps deliberately so. "I have decided for the present to say nothing about the ventricles than that they are hollows or cavities in which air, drawn during inspiration, and vital spirit, transmitted to them by the heart, are altered by the power of the peculiar substance of the brain into animal spirit and this is distributed through the nerves to the organs of the senses and movement. . . ."[38] Actually Vesalius was quite enraged about philosophers who, without having personally examined the brain, endowed the ventricles with intellectual faculties. He singled out Gregor Reisch, author of the *Margarita Philosophica* (Philosopher's Pearl) first issued at Freiburg-im-Breisgau in 1503, although poor Reisch simply reiterated the old story about the site of the mental functions in various ventricles.

Vesalius made the brain rather than the ventricular system the seat of the soul. He even used metaphysical arguments against the latter assumption. How could it be that our intelligence rests in the cerebral ventricles when "the structure of the brain of brutes" and particularly the shape of the ventricular system "resembles that of man?"

Meanwhile, knowledge of the gross anatomy of the brain improved with every new textbook. The second edition of Berengario da Carpi's *Isagogue Breves,* published in 1523, included the first modern although crude illustration of the lateral and third ventricles and choroid plexuses (Fig. 31). By 1543 Vesalius depicted them almost faultlessly (Fig. 32).

Leonardo da Vinci, less hampered by tradition, accustomed to the unusual, and familiar with the casting of bronze statues, performed the wax casting of the cerebral ventricles of an ox. He presented for the first time a three-dimensional form of that system (Fig. 33).[39, 40] Interestingly enough, among Leonardo's

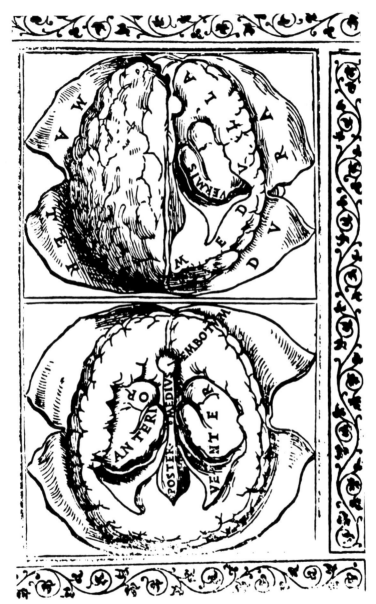

Figure 31. The first modern illustration of the ventricular system and choroid plexus by Berengario da Carpi (*Isagogae Breves*, 1523).

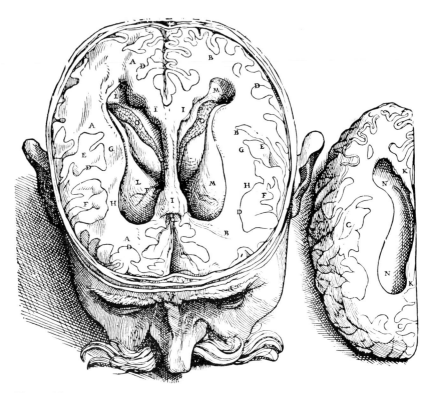

Figure 32. Anatomy of the lateral ventricles and choroid plexus in Vesalius'
De Humani Corporis Fabrica (1543).

sketches in his *Quaderni d' Anatomia*[41] there is one that shows
the customary schematic three-ring picture of the ventricles
(Fig. 34). According to Clark,[42] this was drawn in 1490. However, in a later drawing, dated by Clark as 1504 and performed
therefore following his wax casting, a semblance of the normal
ventricular configuration emerged. Yet, even then he was reluctant to break completely with the past. He scribbled "impren-
siva" over the lateral ventricle, "senso commune" to the third,
and "memor' (ia)" to the fourth.

The trouble was that Leonardo's anatomical knowledge was
without influence not only on his contemporaries, but for several centuries to come. They were deeply buried in manuscript

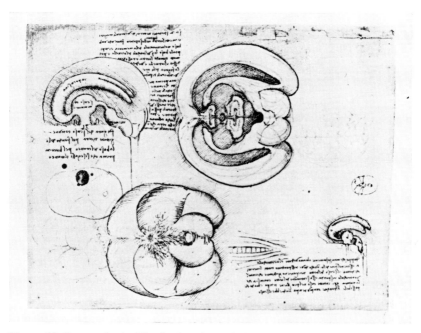

Figure 33. Leonardo da Vinci's drawings of the ventricular system after wax-casting of the ventricles. *Quaderni d'Anatomia,* Q V 7r, ? 1504.

form at the Royal Library of Windsor Castle until the nine-teenth century. Saunders[43] argues this point and believes that one should not ignore the great power of oral tradition in the early years of the modern era. This seems doubtful to me. Authors, such as Berengario da Carpi, Fabricius ab Aquapendente, and Scultetus, were not only well read, but also had the tendency to quote their contemporaries and older authorities by name quite lavishly as a matter of courtesy. Leonardo's name is nowhere to be found.

A similar dichotomy in concept can be found in the works of Berengario da Carpi. Although he rendered the first illustrations of the ventricles in a printed book with any pretension to ac-curacy (Fig. 31), the schematic drawing of them exists on other pages (Fig. 35).

So the rather sophisticated knowledge of the anatomy of the

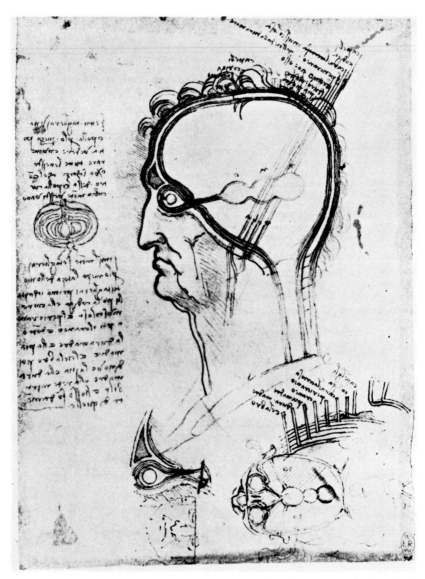

Figure 34. Diagrammatic sagittal section of the head by Leonardo da Vinci with schematic representation of the functional centers of the brain situated in the cerebral ventricles. *Quaderni d' Anatomia,* Q V 6v, ? 1490.

𝕿ractatus de Fractura Caluę Cranei a Carpo editus.

Figure 35. Schematic representation of the ventricular system by Berengario da Carpi in his book on head injuries (*Tractatus de Fractura Calve sive Cranei*, 1518).

ventricular system and the philosophical "trinity of hollow spheres,"[37] perhaps more aptly called *three-ring circus*, continues to be depicted by anatomists and surgeons alike. The only serious attempts made in the seventeenth century were to reconcile this ventricular theory with the unmistakable fact that the brain substance is also involved. In 1664, Willis attempted to combine the spiritual and palpable by correlating the flow of spirit with anatomical structures. He described in fascinating detail the flow of spirit in the brain substance, "inwards for sensation and outwards for the movement."[33] Parts of the brain itself, rather than the cavities within, become the center of function. Imagination presides in the corpus callosum (note the fine difference —rather than in the lateral ventricles!). There is even a "surge progressing from the corpus callosum towards the cortex of the brain." "With the disappearance of phantasy they constitute memory of the thing."

Actually, the concept of spiritual forces in the ventricles continued into the eighteenth century. Although Descartes[44] considered the pineal gland as the seat of the soul, he still reserved the ventricles for the animal spirit. The last person of renown who embued the cerebrospinal fluid with spiritual qualities (he called it "sensorium commune"—common sense) was Sömmerring,[45] the discoverer of the substantia nigra, in 1796.

From their writings, it is obvious that surgeons, such as Paré and Scultetus, were quite aware that the ventricular system is filled with fluid and not air, although there might have been some doubt in their minds whether this fluid is normal or pathological. They were equally familiar with hydrocephalus. According to Scultetus, in obstructive hydrocephalus "the brain substance became very thin . . . to such an extent that the anterior ventricles shine through it." Ambroise Paré described infantile hydrocephalus at autopsy: "I found the brain no larger than a tennis ball. I have never seen one recover when the fluid is very abundant within the head. . . ."[16(p18-19)] Cauterization of the fontanelle over the bregma with removal of cerebrospinal fluid was already practiced.

Penetrating injury to the ventricles was considered deadly by the surgeons, and death was supposed to come quickly. Yet, occasionally the patient lived for a short time. In one of his most remarkable case histories, Ambroise Paré told the story of a soldier who was struck on the head by a halberd at a crooked dice game. The blade of the halberd must have sliced deep into his cerebral hemisphere because it penetrated the left ventricle. Nevertheless, the man remained conscious until a few days later when "during the dressing, he died in my hands in convulsions."[16(p165-166)] Scultetus also considered compression of the hemisphere with its ventricle deadly because then "the ventricles are not able to elaborate the animal spirit" necessary for motor power and sensation throughout the body.

There is evidence of keen observation in Scultetus's writings. He was well aware of the agitation or coma associated with cerebral contusion. Convulsions were well described: "The patient exhibited episodes of wild and confused expression on his face together with convulsions of the limbs. His fists were clenched and the fingers had to be pried open. The impression caused by his nails could be seen in his palms." Hemiplegia contralateral to the contusion or subdural hematoma, sometimes associated with Jacksonian seizures, was noticed, but localized cerebral functions, even the principle of hemispheric dominance and crossing of the major fiber tracts remained a dark secret to them.

NOTES AND REFERENCES

1. Zimmerman, L.M., and Veith, I.: *Great Ideas in the History of Surgery.* Baltimore, Williams and Wilkins, 1961.
2. Strohl, E.L.: Johannes Scultetus (1595-1645). *Arch Surg,* 87:396-397, 1963.
3. Gnudi, M.T., and Webster, J.P.: *The Life and Times of Gaspare Tagliacozzi. Surgeon of Bologna 1549-1599.* New York, H. Reichner, 1950.
4. Nesmith, F.H., Jr.: Ornament and symbolism in early medical books. *JAMA,* 212:109-114, 1970.
5. Daniel, H.: *The World of Jacques Callot.* New York, Lear Publishers, 1948.
6. Plan, P.P.: *Jacques Callot, maitre graveur (1593-1635) suivi d'un catalogue chronologique. Nouvelle édition revue et réduite ornée de 96 estampes et d'un portrait.* Bruxelles and Paris, G. van Oest & Cie., 1914.
7. Wedgewood, C.V.: *The Thirty Years' War.* Garden City, New York, Doubleday, 1961.
8. Trevor-Roper, H.: Why do great wars begin? *Horizon,* 5:32-41, 1962.
9. Hamby, W.B.: *Ambroise Paré. Surgeon of the Renaissance.* St. Louis, Warren H. Green, 1967.
10. Burgess, A.: The anatomy of melancholy. *Horizon,* 12:48-53, 1970.
11. von Clausewitz, K.: In Collins, E.M. (Ed.): *War, Politics, and Power.* Chicago, Henry Regnery, 1962.
12. Courville, C.B.: War wounds of the cranium in the middle ages. II. As noted in the skulls of the Sedlec ossuary near Kuttenberg, Czechoslovakia. *Bull Los Angeles Neurol Soc,* 30:34-44, 1965.
13. Courville, C.B.: War wounds of the cranium in the middle ages. I. As disclosed in the skeletal material from the battle of Wisby (1361 A.D.). *Bull Los Angeles Neurol Soc,* 30:27-33, 1965.
14. Many of these helmeted skulls and chainmailed skeletal remains are on display at the Historical Museum of Stockholm.
15. Payne-Gallwey, Sir Ralph: *The Crossbow. Mediaeval and Modern, Military and Sporting. Its Construction, History and Management.* London, 1903.
16. Hamby, W.B.: *The Case Reports and Autopsy Records of Ambroise Paré.* Springfield, Thomas, 1960, p. 183.
17. Paré, Ambroyse: *La Methode de Traicter Les Playes Traictes par Hacquebutes et Autres Bastions à feu.* 1545.

18. Jackson, H.J.: *European Hand Firearms of the Sixteenth, Seventeenth and Eighteenth Centuries.* London, The Holland Press, 1923.

19. Harford, R.: *A Treatise of Arms. English Military Discipline.* London, 1680.

20. Norman, V.: *Arms and Armour.* London, Weidenfeld and Nicolson, 1964.

21. The bloodstained shirt and jerkin of Gustavus Adolphus, torn by bullets, are preserved to this day in the Nordisk Museum in Stockholm.

22. Leonardo, R.A.: *History of Surgery.* New York, Froben Press, 1943, p. 145.

23. Dott, N. M.: Further reflections on reintegration in specialist medicine. *J Neurosurg*, 33:117-126, 1970.

24. Finlayson, J.: *Account of the Life and Works of Maister Peter Lowe.* Glasgow, James Maclehose and Sons, 1899.

25. John of Mirfield: *Surgery.* (Translated by Colton, J.B., 2nd.) New York, Hafner, 1969.

26. Thompson, C.J.C.: The evolution and development of surgical instruments. IV. The trepan. *Brit J Surg,* 25:726-734, 1938.

27. Walker, A.E.: *A History of Neurological Surgery.* Springfield, Thomas, 1951, pp. 216-247.

28. Incipit cyrurgia edita et compilata a divino fratre Theodorico episcopo Cerviensi ordinis praedicatorum. In *Cyrurgia Guidonis de Cauliaco,* Venice, 1499.

29. Crombie, A.C.: *Medieval and Modern Science. I. Science in the Middle Ages: V-XIII Centuries.* Garden City, New York, Doubleday, 1959.

30. Lisowski, F.P.: Prehistoric and early historic trepanation. In Brothwell, D., and Candison, A.T. (Eds.): *Diseases in Antiquity.* Springfield, Thomas, 1967, pp. 651-672.

31. Loeser, J.D.: History of skeletal traction in the treatment of cervical spine injuries. *J Neurosurg,* 33:54-59, 1970.

32. Gibson, W.C.: Pioneers in localization of function in the brain. *JAMA,* 180:944-951, 1962.

33. Clarke, E., and O'Malley, C.D.: *The Human Brain and Spinal Cord. A Historical Study Illustrated by Writings from Antiquity to the Twentieth Century.* Berkeley and Los Angeles, University of California Press, 1968.

34. Sherrington, Sir Charles: *Man on His Nature,* 2nd ed. Garden City, New York, Doubleday, 1953.

35. Singer, C.: *Vesalius on the Human Brain.* London, Oxford University Press, 1952.

36. Sudhoff, W.: Die Lehre von den Hirnventrikeln in textlicher und graphischer Tradition des Altertums und Mittelalters. *Arch f Gesch Med,* 7:149-205, 1913.

37. Millen, J.W., and Woollam, D.H.M.: *The Anatomy of the Cerebrospinal Fluid.* London, Oxford University Press, 1962.

38. Saunders, J.B. de C.M., and O'Malley, C.D.: *The Illustrations from the*

Works of Andreas Vesalius of Brussels. Cleveland and New York, The World Publishing Co., 1950.

39. O'Malley, C.D., and Saunders, J.B. de C.M.: *Leonardo da Vinci on the Human Body.* New York, Henry Schuman, 1952.
40. MacCurdy, E.: *The Notebooks of Leonardo da Vinci.* New York, George Braziller, 1954.
41. da Vinci, Leonardo: *Quaderni d'Anatomia.* Christiania (Norway), O.C.L. Vangensten, A. Fonahu, and H. Hopstock, 1911-1916, vols. I-VI.
42. Clark, K.: *A Catalogue of the Drawings of Leonardo da Vinci in the Collection of His Majesty the King at Windsor Castle.* Cambridge, 1935.
43. Saunders, J.B. de C.M.: Leonardo da Vinci as anatomist and physiologist: A critical evaluation. *Texas Rep Biol Med,* 13:1010-1026, 1955.
44. Descartes, R.: *Les Passions de l' Ame.* Amsterdam, Elsevier, 1649.
45. Sömmerring, S.T.: *Vom Hirn und Rückenmark.* Mainz, Winkopp, 1788.